INFORMAL ASSESSMENTS FOR TRANSITION

Postsecondary Education and Training

Patricia L. Sitlington

James R. Patton ■ Gary M. Clark

 **pro·ed**
An International Publisher

8700 Shoal Creek Boulevard ■ Austin, Texas 78757-6897 ■ 800/897-3202 ■ Fax 800/397-7633 ■ www.proedinc.com

© 2008 by PRO-ED, Inc.
8700 Shoal Creek Boulevard
Austin, Texas 78757-6897
800/897-3202   Fax 800/397-7633
www.proedinc.com

ISBN-13: 978-1-4164-0337-1

Printed in the United States of America

3   4   5   6   7   8   9   10   17   16   15   14   13   12   11   10

Contents

Introduction

Enrollment in a formal education program after individuals leave high school is a major part of and a next step in their adult lives. Postsecondary education and training can be provided in a number of settings, including 4-year colleges and universities; community and junior colleges; private vocational schools that offer certificates in a particular job area, such as cosmetology or truck driving; apprenticeship programs; on-the-job training programs; adult education programs; and the military.

Informal assessment can help students and their families when they are making the decision to go to a postsecondary education or training program and can also help them prepare for and succeed in their choice of experience. Formal or standardized assessment is not addressed directly; informal assessment, however, is a direct response to the need for ways of asking appropriate questions for the planning process as an alternative to using only testing and other formal or standardized assessment procedures.

Assessment Information Needed at the Secondary Level

The Individuals with Disabilities Education Improvement Act of 2004 (IDEA 2004) requires schools to conduct a transition planning process and defines transition services as a set of coordinated activities

> designed to be within a results-oriented process, that is focused on improving the academic and functional achievement of the child with a disability to facilitate the child's movement from school to post-school activities, including postsecondary education, vocational education, integrated employment (including supported employment), continuing and adult education, adult services, independent living, or community participation. (§300.43(a)(1))

These activities must be "based on the individual child's needs, taking into account the child's strengths, preferences, and interests" (§300.43(a)(2)).

IDEA 2004 also makes it clear that assessment for transition planning is essential. The law requires that, for individuals 16 years of age and older, the Individualized Education Program (IEP) must include the following:

- Appropriate measurable postsecondary goals based upon age-appropriate transition assessments related to training, education, employment, and where appropriate, independent living skills; and
- The transition services (including courses of study) needed to assist the child in reaching those goals. (§300.320(b))

The new language for the schools' mandate to provide age-appropriate assessment information for the IEP and transition planning gives new focus to what has been a basic component of the IEP since it was instituted—the information needed to determine how a student is currently performing, now referred to as Present Level of

Academic Achievement and Functional Performance. Now that appropriate assessment for both academic achievement and functional performance is required, we need new ways of providing such information.

Practical Implications of Transition Assessment

Students pursuing postsecondary education will encounter a host of challenges, and they and their families need opportunities to engage in the wide range of topics associated with postsecondary education and to plan, as best as possible, for the student's smooth transition to this setting. A key component of doing this successfully involves assessment. The transition assessment process can and should begin in middle school to get students thinking about what they might do when they complete high school. Middle and junior high school teachers especially can begin informal assessments to initiate students' thinking about high school expectations and demands, motivate students' thinking about occupational choices and their implications for schooling, and provide high school teachers with baseline information for high school planning and instruction. When a student approaches age 16, schools should conduct a thorough assessment, using either formal or informal methods, with the goal of identifying the student's interests, preferences, strengths, and needs as they relate to what will happen when school is completed.

Methods for Gathering Information

There are a number of methods that may be used to gather information on the strengths, needs, preferences, and interests of the student. There are also a number of methods to gather information on the demands of postsecondary education programs and environments, and the supports available within these environments (Clark, 2007; Sitlington & Clark, 2007; Sitlington, Neubert, Begun, Lombard, & Leconte, 2007; Whitfield, Feller, & Wood, 2007). Methods for gathering information on the student include background information; interviews; rating scales (formal and informal); paper-and-pencil tests (formal and informal); performance samples; behavioral observation; and situational assessments (observing students in actual postsecondary environments). These sources also provide information on the demands of postsecondary education and training programs. The instruments included in this book could be used as part of a number of these approaches.

Summarizing the Information Available at the Secondary Level

Two specific summary statements help in organizing the information available at the secondary level so it meets the needs of postsecondary education and training programs.

First, IDEA 2004 mandated that a Summary of Performance (SOP) be provided for each student as he/she exits the school system, which must provide a summary of

- the student's academic achievement and functional performance, and
- recommendations on how to assist the student to meet his/her postsecondary goals.

The SOP provides a way for school systems to compile assessment data and provide students and their families valuable information that students can share with postsecondary education and training programs.

Many states and districts have developed a standard format for the SOP. The National Transition Assessment Summit (Dukes, Shaw, & Madaus, 2007) developed a format that focuses on summarizing data from formal assessments but also includes informal assessment information. One state example, the Iowa Department of Education's (2007) "Summary for Postsecondary Living, Learning, and Working," focuses on summarizing information primarily from informal assessments but also uses existing formal assessment data.

Many states are also developing formats to assist students in requesting accommodations at the postsecondary level. The Appendix presents an example (a blank form and a completed form) of a *Support for Accommodation Request*, developed by a statewide group of secondary and postsecondary practitioners and other adult providers (Iowa Department of Education, 2005). The purpose of this document is to support the student's request for accommodations at the postsecondary level, using information from the student's performance at the secondary level and the accommodations and supports found effective at that level.

Challenges to Providing Information

Three specific innovations in special education have created challenges in the transition of students with disabilities from secondary to postsecondary education (Kincaid, 1997; Sitlington, 2003; Sitlington & Clark, 2006). First, under the Individuals with Disabilities Education Act Amendments of 1997 (IDEA 1997), a district is no longer obligated to conduct a 3-year reevaluation if the IEP team determines that it is unnecessary to do so for eligibility purposes. The regulations also indicate that an exit evaluation is not required for students whose eligibility for special education will terminate due to either graduation or exceeding age eligibility. These regulations will likely lead to students leaving high school with increasingly older formal documentation of their disability (Madaus & Shaw, 2007). This may mean that for many adolescents in their last year of high school, the last formal evaluation data collected on the student may be years old when the student graduates. As Sitlington and Payne (2004) pointed out, however, this does not mean that ongoing data have not been collected, although these data may be of a more informal nature.

Second, special educators in many states are moving away from emphasizing standardized assessments and toward the use of curriculum-based assessments. Such assessments are important in middle and high school because they are criterion referenced and align with school instructional standards. These curriculum-based assessments also may provide a great deal of information to postsecondary institutions in terms of the student's level of mastery in specific content areas and in comparing the student's performance to students with and without disabilities in the district.

Finally, many states are moving away from specific disability labels and toward the concept of "student in need of special education," or a noncategorical label. Although a specific label such as "learning disability" may not be applied to the student, documentation should be provided that shows that the student's disability substantially limits his or her learning. Thus, although these more recent changes and trends pose challenges to the smooth transition of adolescents with disabilities into post-secondary education, they also promise data that may be more recent and more relevant (Sitlington & Payne, 2004). The challenge is to identify how to convert the data currently being gathered at the secondary level into information that is needed by postsecondary institutions.

Changes Holding Promise

The IDEA Amendments of 1997 require that all students with disabilities be included in state or district assessments that are required of other students. In addition, the IEP must include a statement that addresses the issue of participation in state or district-wide assessments (Bryant, Patton, & Vaughn, 2000). The No Child Left Behind Act of 2001 requires that all states assess students in reading and mathematics in Grades 3 to 8, and at least once between Grades 10 and 12. States must also assess students in science at least once in elementary, middle, and high school. This should provide information on how students with disabilities compare to those without disabilities in their district and their state. States and local districts are also increasing their graduation requirements to include more rigorous coursework and tests to demonstrate knowledge and skills needed after high school (Kochhar-Bryant & Bassett, 2002).

In addition, the Association for Higher Education and Disability (AHEAD; 2004), the Educational Testing Service (ETS; 2005), and the National Joint Committee on Learning Disabilities (2007) have all issued statements that are closer to acknowledging the role of informal assessments in documenting a student's disability and determining the accommodations and supports needed.

Assessment Information Needed at the Postsecondary Level

According to Sitlington et al. (2007), transition assessment means

> an ongoing process of collecting information on the student's strengths, needs, preferences, and interests as they relate to the demands of current and future living, learning, and working environments. This process should begin in middle school and continue until the student graduates or exits high school. Information from this process should be used to drive the IEP (Individualized Education Program) and transition planning process and to develop the Summary of Performance document detailing the student's academic and functional performance and postsecondary goals. (pp. 2–3)

Postsecondary institutions use assessment information in two principal ways. First, to determine if the individual has a disability, as defined by Section 504 of the Rehabilitation Act of 1973 and the Americans with Disabilities Act of 1990 (to document a disability, students must first provide evidence that their disability substantially limits a major life activity; e.g., their learning). Second, students need to demonstrate that they are otherwise qualified, that is, are able to meet the essential requirements of the program when provided reasonable accommodations (Sitlington & Payne, 2004).

The issue of who is otherwise qualified can be complicated. Scott (1991) proposed three questions to address the issue of who is "otherwise qualified":

- What are the program or course requirements?
- What nonessential criteria can be accommodated without changing the essence of the course or program?
- What are the specific abilities and disabilities of the student within this context?

Postsecondary education and training programs also use documentation to help determine appropriate and reasonable accommodations based on the individual's specific, disability-related needs (Hatzes, Reiff, & Bramel, 2002). Accommodations may take place at the program level and often include part-time schedules, longer time to complete the program, and priority registration. Accommodations may also be directly related to instruction and course-related methods and commonly include activities such as changes to the testing or evaluation procedures, the use of assistive technology, recorded books or a reader, tape-recorded lectures, and notetaking adaptations (Mull & Sitlington, 2003; Mull, Sitlington & Alper, 2001).

Once a student has sufficiently documented that he or she has a qualifying disability, a postsecondary institution is responsible for providing reasonable accommodations that "do not result in unfair advantage, require significant alteration to the program or activity, result in the lowering of academic or technical standards, or cause the college to incur undue financial hardship" (Thomas, 2000, p. 254).

About This Book

This book is the third of three companion books to *Informal Assessments for Transition Planning* (Clark, Patton, & Moulton, 2000). The first companion book is *Employment and Career Planning* (Synatschk, Clark, Patton, & Copeland, 2007); the second book is *Independent Living and Community Participation* (Synatschk, Clark, & Patton, 2008). Each of these books can be used separately or in combination with the others in the series.

These books extend the Comprehensive Informal Inventory of Knowledge and Skills for Transition and the 45 informal assessments found in *Informal Assessments for Transition Planning* (Clark et al., 2000); these assessments cut across the nine transition planning domains of the *Transition Planning Inventory* (Clark & Patton, 2006). Conceptually, all were designed to move from the general information of the *Transition Planning Inventory* to more specific assessment of areas that appear to be missing, unknown, or were uncertain due to discrepancies in information.

This book provides 64 informal instruments that we have found, edited, or developed, and for which reproduction permission has been granted for educational purposes. These instruments may be used to collect information on the student's strengths, needs, preferences, and interests or in collecting information on the demands of postsecondary education and training programs and supports available within these programs.

These informal assessments are organized into five topical areas (defined in the following paragraphs) that are critical to transition planning and decision making. Each assessment is designed to be completed by the student, family members, or educators at the secondary or postsecondary level.

The Big Picture: Getting My Future in Focus

Informal instruments in this section focus on big-picture goals and would be useful to the student early in the process of thinking about postsecondary education and training. Areas covered include identifying overall goals, developing a plan of action, and assessing readiness for postsecondary education and training.

Self-Determination: Understanding and Evaluating Myself

Areas covered in this section include understanding the student's disability, documenting a disability, identifying the student's strengths and challenges, and determining the best instructional formats for the student.

Planning for Postsecondary Education/Training: Preparing for My Future

Areas covered in this section include factors to consider when selecting a postsecondary education and training program and when applying for postsecondary education and financial aid.

Academic Skills and Support Needs: Addressing Learning-Related Demands

Instruments in this area focus on identifying specific study skills, academic skills, the demands of classrooms, and supports and accommodations needed by the student. They also focus on learning strengths, needs, and styles.

Nonacademic Support Needs: Examining the Other Parts of My Life

Instruments in this section focus on areas such as comparing costs of colleges, accessing campus activities outside of class, and independent living skills.

A Final Note

The transition process through public school levels and the transition process from public school to postsecondary education and training are responsibilities shared among students, their family members, and educators. Asking students age-appropriate, student-focused questions about their dreams, interests, preferences, strengths, and needs is usually highly appreciated and is rarely considered an intrusion of privacy; for many students, these questions show a rare indicator of caring from the school.

We hope these instruments will assist you as teachers or counselors as you plan, with students and their families, for secondary school educational goals in the IEP, course of study choices, and postsecondary education and training planning.

References

Americans with Disabilities Act of 1990, 42 U.S.C. §12101 *et seq.* (1990)

Association for Higher Education and Disability. (2004). *AHEAD best practices: Disability documentation in higher education.* Retrieved July 16, 2007, from www.ahead.org/resources/bestpracticesdoc.htm

Bryant, D. P., Patton, J. R., & Vaughn, S. (2000). *Step-by-step guide for including students with disabilities in state and districtwide assessments.* Austin, TX: PRO-ED.

Clark, G. M. (2007). *Assessment for transitions planning* (2nd ed.). Austin, TX: PRO-ED.

Clark, G. M., & Patton, J. R. (2006). *Transition planning inventory—Updated version.* Austin, TX: PRO-ED.

Clark, G. M., Patton, J. R., & Moulton, L. R. (2000). *Informal assessments for transition planning.* Austin, TX: PRO-ED.

Dukes, L. L., Shaw, S. F., & Madaus, J. W. (2007). How to complete a summary of performance for students exiting to postsecondary education. *Assessment for Effective Intervention, 32*(3), 143–159.

Educational Testing Service. (2005, November). *New policy regarding LD and LD/ADHD documentation shelf life.* Retrieved July 17, 2007, from http://www.ets.org/portal/site/ets/menuitem.c988ba0e5dd572bada20

Hatzes, N. M., Reiff, H. B., & Bramel, M. H. (2002). The documentation dilemma: Access and accommodations for postsecondary students with learning disabilities. *Assessment for Effective Intervention, 27*(3), 37–52.

Individuals with Disabilities Education Act of 1990, 20 U.S.C. §1400 *et seq.* (1990) (amended 1997)

Individuals with Disabilities Education Improvement Act of 2004, 20 U.S.C. §1400 *et seq.* (2004) (reauthorization of the Individuals with Disabilities Education Act of 1990)

Iowa Department of Education. (2005). *Support for accommodation request.* Des Moines, IA: Author.

Iowa Department of Education. (2007). Summary for postsecondary living, learning, and working. In P. L. Sitlington, D. A. Neubert, W. H. Begun, R. C. Lombard, & P. J. Leconte (2007), *Assess for success: A practitioner's handbook on transition assessment* (2nd ed.; pp. 125–128). Thousand Oaks, CA: Corwin Press.

Kincaid, J. M. (1997). IDEA revisions may have "ripple effect" on college transition. *Disability Compliance for Higher Education, 3*(4), 1, 6–7.

Kochhar-Bryant, C. A., & Bassett, D. S. (2002). Challenge and promise in aligning transition and standards-based education. In C. A. Kochhar-Bryant & D. S. Bassett (Eds.), *Aligning transition and standards-based education: Issues and strategies* (pp. 1–23). Arlington, VA: Council for Exceptional Children.

Madaus, J. W., & Shaw, S. F. (2007). Transition assessment: An introduction to the special issue. *Assessment for Effective Intervention, 32*(3), 130–132.

Miller, R. J., Lombard, R. C., & Corbey, S. A. (2007). *Transition assessment: Planning transition and IEP development for youth with mild to moderate disabilities.* Boston: Allyn & Bacon.

Mull, C., & Sitlington, P. L. (2003). The role of technology in the transition to postsecondary education of students with learning disabilities: A review of the literature. *The Journal of Special Education, 37*(1), 26–32.

Mull, C., Sitlington, P. L., & Alper, S. A. (2001). Postsecondary education for students with learning disabilities. *Exceptional Children, 68*(1), 97–118.

National Joint Committee on Learning Disabilities. (2007). *The documentation disconnect for students with learning disabilities: Improving access to postsecondary disability services. A report from the National Joint Committee on Learning Disabilities.* Retrieved July 16, 2007, from http://ahead.org/resources/njld.paper.php

No Child Left Behind Act of 2001, 20 U.S.C. §6301 *et seq.* (2002)

Rehabilitation Act of 1973, 29 U.S.C. §701 *et seq.*

Scott, S. (1991). A change in legal status: An overlooked dimension in the transition to higher education. *Journal of Learning Disabilities, 24,* 459–466.

Sitlington, P. L. (2003). Postsecondary education: The other transition. *Exceptionality, 11*(2), 103–113.

Sitlington, P. L., & Clark, G. M. (2006). *Transition education and services for students with disabilities* (4th ed.). Boston: Allyn & Bacon.

Sitlington, P. L., & Clark, G. M. (2007). The transition assessment process and IDEIA 2004. *Assessment for Effective Intervention, 32*(3), 133–142.

Sitlington, P. L., Neubert, D. A., Begun, W. H., Lombard, R. C., & Leconte, P. J. (2007). *Assess for success: A practitioner's handbook on transition assessment* (2nd ed.). Thousand Oaks, CA: Corwin Press.

Sitlington, P. L., & Payne, E. M. (2004). Information needed by postsecondary education: Can we provide it as part of the transition assessment process? *Learning Disabilities: A Contemporary Journal, 2*(2), 1–14.

Synatschk, K. O., Clark, G. M., & Patton, J. R. (2008). *Independent living and community participation.* Austin, TX: PRO-ED.

Synatschk, K. O., Clark, G. M., Patton, J. R., & Copeland, L. R. (2007). *Employment and career planning.* Austin, TX: PRO-ED.

Thomas, S. B. (2000). College students and disability law. *Journal of Special Education, 33,* 248–257.

Webb, K. W. (2000). *Transition to postsecondary education: Strategies for students with disabilities.* Austin, TX: PRO-ED.

Whitfield, E. A., Feller, R., & Wood, C. (2007). *A counselor's guide to career assessment instruments* (5th ed.). Columbus, OH: National Career Development Association.

Author Note

An exhaustive and thorough attempt was made to determine the original source of all documents used in this book. In a few cases, however, the original source was never identified. We apologize if we failed to provide adequate information for the source of a particular document. If the original source is discovered, we will include that information in future printings of the book. If you know the source of a document, please contact PRO-ED (editorial@proedinc.com).

The Big Picture: Getting My Future in Focus

List of Inventories

Name _____   Date _____

Consumer Guide to Transition Planning

☀ **Respond to the following questions.**

1. When do you think you will finish high school? _____

2. Do you plan to graduate with a diploma? _____

3. Do you want to have a job when you finish high school? _____

4. Where do you want to work after you leave high school? _____

5. What kind of help might you need to get a job after high school? _____

   _____

6. Do you want to go on to school or further training when you finish high school? _____

7. Where would you like to go to school after high school? _____

8. What kind of help might you need to go to school after high school? _____

   _____

9. Where do you want to live after you leave high school? _____

10. What kind of help would you need to live where you want after high school? _____

    _____

11. What do you do for fun now? _____

    _____

12. What would you like to do for fun after you leave high school? _____

    _____

13. How will you travel to and from your job and community activities? _____

14. Do you take prescription medications or have any health and medical concerns? _____

15. If yes, please describe dosage or health and medical concerns. _____

    _____

16. How will you pay for health and medical care? _____

17. How much money will you need to live on? _____

18. Where will you get the money needed to live in the community? _____

Source: Illinois Transition Project, by Governor's Planning Council on Developmental Disabilities, Springfield, IL: Author. Adapted with permission.

What Are My Values?

☼ **Circle the star beside the 10 values that are the most important to you. Then go back over these 10 values and choose the top five by writing the numbers 1 through 5 on the line beside each one (1 =** *the most important to you of these five* **and 5 =** *the least important to you of these five*).

_____ ★ Having good friendships and getting along well with people

_____ ★ Having a positive relationship with a spouse or a romantic partner

_____ ★ Having self-respect

_____ ★ Being well-off financially

_____ ★ Having a good spiritual life

_____ ★ Being competent at my work

_____ ★ Having the respect of others

_____ ★ Making an important contribution to humankind

_____ ★ Being a moral person (i.e., doing the right thing)

_____ ★ Feeling secure

_____ ★ Being a great athlete

_____ ★ Being physically active

_____ ★ Being creative

_____ ★ Having freedom and independence

_____ ★ Being well-educated

_____ ★ Contributing to the welfare of others

_____ ★ Having peace of mind

_____ ★ Getting recognition or becoming famous

_____ ★ Being happy

_____ ★ Enjoying leisure time

_____ ★ Being a good citizen

_____ ★ Living a healthy lifestyle

_____ ★ Being intelligent

_____ ★ Developing good family relationships

_____ ★ Being honest and having integrity

_____ ★ Showing dedication and commitment

_____ ★ Having personal responsibility

Source: What Are My Values? Retrieved January 31, 2008, from www.wadsworth.com/cgi-wadsworth/course_products_wp.pl?fid=M691&product_isbn_
issn=0534608043&chapter_number=1&resource_id=691&module_id=1501

Student _____   Parent/Guardian _____

IEP Team Leader _____   IEP Conference Date _____

IEP Preconference Interview Question Guide

☼ **Read each question out loud.**

Student Questions

1 What do you think are your learning strengths?

_____

2 What do you think are your greatest challenges related to learning?

_____

3 What goals do you want to work on next year to help you do better in school, now and in the future?

_____

Parent/Guardian Questions

1 What do you see as (*student's name*) greatest strengths?

_____

2 What skills would you like to see (*student's name*) improve or learn over the next year?

_____

3 What goals would you like (*student's name*) to pursue?

_____

4 Is there anything we have overlooked or something else you'd like to say about (*student's name*) learning needs or career interests?

_____

5 Is there any other area about the future that concerns you?

_____

Source: Education Conference Question Guide (p. 3), by A. K. Van Reusen, C. S. Bos, J. B. Schumaker, and D. D. Deshler, 1994, Lawrence, KS: Edge Enterprises. Copyright 1994 by Edge Enterprises. Adapted with permission.

Making a Decision on a Course of Study Major

☀ Choose a major area of study that interests you the most right now, and then answer the questions for this choice of major. When you have finished, state whether this major is a good match for you.

Name of course of study major _____

(Examples: English, math, Spanish, architecture, political science, journalism)

Preferences and Interests

- How does this major match up with my high school courses that I enjoyed and experienced success in?

  _____

Aptitudes and Abilities

- Which abilities do I have that are needed in this major?

  _____

Educational Considerations

- What requirements for pursuing this major have I already completed?

  _____

- What courses must I complete in order to advance successfully in this major?

  _____
  _____

- Considering my high school attendance and grades, are these educational and training requirements realistic for me?

  _____

- How will the number of hours and the time of day studying or completing assignments match my desired lifestyle?

  _____

- How will I be able to afford the cost of this educational program major?

  _____

- Am I willing to change majors, even if it will take longer to complete my college program?

  _____

Career Outlook for this Major

- How do the data-people-things requirements in the courses for this major match up with my own career preferences?

  _____

- What are the career options with this major?

  _____
  _____

- What is the projected need for graduates of this major at the time I am ready to graduate and start work?

  _____

- What is the long-term career outlook for this major?

  _____

Narrowing Major Choices

- How is this major a wise choice for me right now?

  _____
  _____

- What are some back-up major choices that are related to this choice of a major?

  _____

Name _____ Date _____

My Postsecondary Plans

☀ **Think about your short-term and long-term plans.**

1. I plan to graduate from high school in _____

2. My ideas and dreams for a job/career are _____

   _____

3. The summer after I graduate, I plan to _____

   _____

4. The first year after I graduate from high school, I plan to _____

   _____

5. Five years after high school graduation, I want to be doing _____

   _____

6. Ten years after high school graduation, I want to be doing _____

   _____

7. I need help with my postsecondary plans in the following ways: _____

   _____

   _____

Source: Tools for Transition: Preparing Students with Learning Disabilities for Postsecondary Education, Ages 13–20 (p. 2), by E. Aune and J. Ness, 1991, Circle Pines, MN: AGS.
Copyright 1991 by AGS. Adapted with permission.

Name _____ Date _____

What Are My Goals?

☼ Your values can help you formulate your goals. Remember that goals can be academic or personal. A good strategy is to set goals that are challenging but achievable. Be sure to make your goals as specific as possible. Complete the following statements to get a better idea of what your goals are.

My main goals in life are

_____

_____

_____

_____

My main goals for the semester are

_____

_____

_____

_____

My main goals for the week are

_____

_____

_____

_____

My main goals for tomorrow are

_____

_____

_____

_____

Source: *What Are My Goals?* Retrieved January 31, 2008, from www.wadsworth.com/cgi-wadsworth/course_products_wp.pl?fid=M691&product_isbn_issn=0534608043&chapter_number=1&resource_id=691&module_id=1502

Name _____ Date _____

My Plan of Action

☼ **List your goals as you see them now.**

Short-Range Goals for This Year

- ◼ _____
- ◼ _____
- ◼ _____
- ◼ _____

I expect to complete these goals by _____

Medium-Range Goals for the Next 2–3 Years

- ◼ _____
- ◼ _____
- ◼ _____
- ◼ _____

I expect to complete these goals by _____

Long-Range Goals for the Next 3–6 Years

- ◼ _____
- ◼ _____
- ◼ _____
- ◼ _____

I expect to complete these goals by _____

Ultimate Career Goals After Postsecondary Education or Training

- ◼ _____
- ◼ _____
- ◼ _____
- ◼ _____

I expect to complete these goals by _____

Source: Copyright 2008 by Gary M. Clark. Used with permission.

Name _____   Date _____

Comparison of High School and College

☼ **Compare the differences between high school and college on the following key dimensions.**

Characteristics	High School	College
Time in class		
Size of class		
Campus size		
Interaction with teacher		
Assignments		
Study time		
Tests		
Attendance in class		
Teaching style		
Notetaking		
Library use		
Independent thinking		
Time management		
Freedom		
Resources and support		
Social environment		

Source: Transition to Postsecondary Education: Strategies for Students with Disabilities (p. 34), by K. W. Webb, 2000, Austin, TX: PRO-ED. Copyright 2000 by PRO-ED, Inc. Adapted with permission.

Planning for After College

☀ **Respond to each of the following statements.**

Five years after graduation, I see myself . . .

_____

_____

_____

Three strengths/skills I see in myself . . .

_____

_____

_____

I can use my strengths/skills in the following jobs/careers:

_____

_____

_____

I am interested in the following jobs/careers:

_____

_____

_____

College can help me reach my goals by . . .

_____

_____

_____

Source: Discussion Guide/Future Planning (Activity 21). Retrieved January 25, 2008, from www.postitt.org/activities/TM_worksheets.pdf

Name _____ Date _____

Why Am I Going to College?

☼ **Think for a few moments about why you want to go to college. Place a check in the box by the items that you feel are benefits of going to college.**

I'm going to college because . . .

☐ It can help me learn and think more effectively.

☐ It can help me get a good job.

☐ It can help me make a lot of money.

☐ I'm avoiding having to find a job.

☐ It's a good place to find a mate.

☐ I want to have a good time.

☐ It's a way to prove my self-worth.

☐ It's a way to get away from home.

☐ My friends will be going to college.

☐ There are things that I can learn there better than anywhere else.

☐ I want to learn more about what I can do with my life.

☐ I couldn't think of anything else to do at this point.

☐ Other _____

☐ Other _____

☼ **Reflect on the reasons that are motivating you to go to college. Are these the best reasons to go to college? To succeed in the academic aspects of college, do you need to rethink your motivation? Evaluate your reasons, and write your evaluation in the space below.**

_____

_____

_____

Source: Why am I here? Retrieved January 31, 2008, from www.wadsworth.com/cgi-wadsworth/course_products_wp.pl?fid=M691&product_isbn_ issn=0534608043&chapter_number=1&resource_id=691&module_id=1500

Name _____   Date _____

High School to College Transition Questionnaire

☼ **Circle the response for each item that best fits you. Then, go back and write totals for each area in the spaces provided.**

General Preparation

	Yes	Not Sure	No
1. I know which college I'd like to attend.	1	3	5
2. I know what I want to study in college.	1	3	5
3. I have met with or spoken to a representative from the college that I would like to attend.	1	3	5
4. I have filled out a college application.	1	3	5
5. I have a plan in place if I find that college is not for me.	1	3	5
6. I know where I will be living during college.	1	3	5
7. I already have made living arrangements for college.	1	3	5
8. I know all the differences between high school and college.	1	3	5
9. I have taken college entrance exams.	1	3	5
10. I feel confident that I will be successful in college.	1	3	5
Total	____	____	____
Grand Total		_____	

Academic Preparation

	Yes	Not Sure	No
11. My current academic plan is designed to help me prepare for college.	1	3	5
12. I have taken the classes needed in high school to prepare me for college.	1	3	5
13. I have taken 4 years of English.	1	3	5
14. I have taken 4 years of Math.	1	3	5
15. I have taken an English composition class.	1	3	5
16. I have taken a math class equal to or higher than Algebra II.	1	3	5
17. My teachers have helped me to prepare for college.	1	3	5
18. I feel my study habits and study skills will help me be successful in college.	1	3	5
19. I scored above an 800 on the SAT college entrance exam.	1	3	5
20. I have a 2.0 or better grade point average.	1	3	5
Total	____	____	____
Grand Total		_____	

➲

Source: High School to College Transition Questionnaire, by C. M. White, 2001. Copyright 2001 by author. Adapted with permission.

Advocacy/Self-Determination

	Yes	Not Sure	No
21. I know which skills I need to improve in order to be successful in college.	1	3	5
22. I know how to advocate for myself.	1	3	5
23. I know the laws that protect my rights.	1	3	5
24. I know how to ensure that my legal rights are guaranteed.	1	3	5
25. I am aware that I, not my parents, need to initiate a request for disability services at college. .	1	3	5
26. I will seek assistance at the office of Services for Students with Disabilities at the institution I attend, if needed.	1	3	5
27. I will seek assistance from instructors, if needed.	1	3	5
28. I know my academic strengths.	1	3	5
29. I know my academic needs and challenges.	1	3	5
30. I know and will request the adaptations/modifications that I need to be successful in college.	1	3	5
Total	____	____	____
Grand Total	_____		

Academic Adaptations/Modifications and Needs

	Yes	Not Sure	No
31. My current IEP includes academic adaptations/modifications.	1	3	5
32. My Summary of Performance document lists specific adaptations that I will need.	1	3	5
33. I can identify the adaptations/modifications/supports I need to be successful in college. . . .	1	3	5
34. I can identify the specific tools I need for reading.	1	3	5
35. I can identify the specific tools that I need for writing.	1	3	5
36. I can identify specific technological adaptations needed to help me be successful in college.	1	3	5
37. I can identify specific adaptations of assignments needed to help me be successful in college.	1	3	5
38. I can identify specific teaching/instructor styles that will help me be successful in college. . . .	1	3	5
39. I know how to adjust to different teaching styles.	1	3	5
40. I can identify my learning style preferences.	1	3	5
Total	____	____	____
Grand Total	_____		

Self-Sufficiency

	Yes	Not Sure	No
41. I know how to budget my money.	1	3	5
42. I know how to manage a bank account.	1	3	5
43. I know how to use a course catalog.	1	3	5
44. I know how to use a computer for course-related work.	1	3	5
45. I know how to take care of all my personal needs.	1	3	5
46. I know how to schedule an appointment.	1	3	5

Source: High School to College Transition Questionnaire, by C. M. White, 2001. Copyright 2001 by author. Adapted with permission.

	Yes	Not Sure	No
47. I know how to use public transportation.	1	3	5
48. I know how to access student health services at college.	1	3	5
49. I know how to use postal services.	1	3	5
50. I am able to fill out all necessary paperwork for college independently.	1	3	5
Total	____	____	____
Grand Total	_____		

Financial Considerations

	Yes	Not Sure	No
51. I am aware of all of the expenses involved in going to college.	1	3	5
52. I will pay for or contribute to the costs of my college education.	1	3	5
53. I know how much college is going to cost me.	1	3	5
54. I know how to apply for financial aid to continue my education.	1	3	5
55. I have completed the necessary financial aid paperwork.	1	3	5
56. I have applied for grants to help pay for college.	1	3	5
57. I have applied for scholarships to help me pay for college.	1	3	5
58. I am willing to work to help pay for college.	1	3	5
59. I am willing to be in a work study program.	1	3	5
60. I understand how working might impact my education.	1	3	5
Total	____	____	____
Grand Total	_____		

Social Skills

	Yes	Not Sure	No
61. I have the skills to make new friends.	1	3	5
62. I make new friends easily.	1	3	5
63. I plan on making new friends when I go to college.	1	3	5
64. I believe I can get along with a roommate.	1	3	5
65. I plan on maintaining old friendships while in college.	1	3	5
66. I am comfortable meeting new people.	1	3	5
67. I have the social skills to participate in study groups.	1	3	5
68. I prefer to work independently.	1	3	5
69. I prefer to work with groups.	1	3	5
70. Peer groups are important to me.	1	3	5
Total	____	____	____
Grand Total	_____		

Source: High School to College Transition Questionnaire, by C. M. White, 2001. Copyright 2001 by author. Adapted with permission.

Family Support ....

		Yes	Not Sure	No
71.	My family is aware that I want to go to college.	1	3	5
72.	My family and I have discussed which college I'd like to attend.	1	3	5
73.	My family is going to help me pay for college.	1	3	5
74.	I can live at home if I want to during college.	1	3	5
75.	My family has been very supportive about my going to college.	1	3	5
76.	I can go to my family for help if I have problems while attending college.	1	3	5
77.	My family has helped me to prepare for college.	1	3	5
78.	My family will support me if I decide that college is not for me.	1	3	5
79.	My family understands all that is involved with my going to college.	1	3	5
80.	Other members of my immediate family have attended college.	1	3	5

Total _____ _____ _____

Grand Total _____

Source: High School to College Transition Questionnaire, by C. M. White, 2001. Copyright 2001 by author. Adapted with permission.

Name _____   Date _____

Summary Sheet

☼ **Transfer the scores from the *High School to College Transition Questionnaire* to the corresponding category below. Place a check mark in the box beside any category that has a score of 25 or higher. Then, total all of the categories.**

❑ General Preparation   _____

❑ Academic Preparation   _____

❑ Advocacy/Self-Determination   _____

❑ Academic Adaptations/Modifications and Needs   _____

❑ Self-Sufficiency   _____

❑ Financial Considerations   _____

❑ Social Skills   _____

❑ Family Support   _____

                              Total Score   _____

*A Total Score of 200 or higher should result in a thorough examination of each category
to determine specific areas of concern.*

☼ **List all checked categories from the highest score to the lowest score. These are the areas of concern that need to be addressed before I enter college.**

Areas of Concern	Plan to Address Concern
_____	_____
_____	_____
_____	_____
_____	_____
_____	_____
_____	_____
_____	_____

Source: Assessing Postsecondary Readiness Skills of Students with Disabilities, by C. M. White, 2001. Copyright 2001 by author. Adapted with permission.

Self-Determination: Understanding and Evaluating Myself

List of Inventories

Understanding My Disability

☀ **Please complete each section.**

My disability is:

_____

_____

_____

My disability affects my ability to *learn* in the following ways:

_____

_____

_____

My disability affects my ability to *live* in the following ways:

_____

_____

_____

My disability affects my ability to *work* in the following ways:

_____

_____

_____

I learn best when:

_____

_____

_____

Documentation of my disability supports the use of the following accommodations:

_____

_____

_____

Source: Activity 8 Worksheet—Self-Advocacy Speech. (n.d.). Retrieved January 25, 2008, from www.postitt.org/activities/TM_worksheets.pdf

Name _____   Date _____

Grade _____   Age _____

Post–IEP Planning: Student

☀ **Circle the number that indicates your current level of knowledge or ability in the areas listed.**

Rating Scale: 1 = *No knowledge or ability*
2 = *Some knowledge or ability*
3 = *High level of knowledge or ability*

Self-Advocacy

You understand your disability, learning strengths, and related accommodations and have the skill to self-advocate in the academic setting.

You have identified

- Your disability (What is it? How does it affect you in the classroom?).   1   2   3
- Your learning strengths (How do you learn best?).   1   2   3
- Appropriate accommodations based on disability and learning strengths   1   2   3
- How your disability documentation supports specific accommodations.   1   2   3
- How to practice self-advocacy in the high school/college setting   1   2   3

Assistive Technology

You understand how assistive technology can effectively accommodate your limitations.

You have an understanding of

- The assistive technology you currently use   1   2   3
- Assistive technology and how it can be used to accommodate learning   1   2   3
- How everyday items can be used as assistive technology.   1   2   3
- Which high technologies can assist you in learning   1   2   3

Planning

You have established a realistic college education goal and have prepared a timeline for successful transition to college.

You have identified

- Personal interests   1   2   3
- Possible career choices   1   2   3
- A college goal based on your interests and strengths   1   2   3
- An academic program that will allow you to meet your college goal.   1   2   3
- A high school timeline of college planning and application activities.   1   2   3

➡

Source: Planning Worksheet: Student Version. Retrieved January 25, 2008, from www.postitt.org/activities/TM_worksheets.pdf

Rating Scale: 1 = *No knowledge or ability*
2 = *Some knowledge or ability*
3 = *High level of knowledge or ability*

Applying to College

You have finished the college admissions process, including identifying appropriate college programs, completing admission criteria, completing financial aid applications, and providing appropriate disability documentation.

You have identified

• Colleges that match interests with academic programs and support needs	1	2	3
• Admission requirements in colleges of interest	1	2	3
• Differences in support services among colleges	1	2	3

You have completed

• Precollege admissions and/or placement testing (SAT; ACT; ASSET)	1	2	3
• Competitive college applications, supporting letters, and essays	1	2	3
• Financial-aid application	1	2	3
• Establishing eligibility for services by meeting with the Disability Support Services coordinator, once accepted at a college	1	2	3

Accessing Support on a College Campus

You understand the changing roles and responsibilities of the student and school in providing disability services in college.

You have an understanding of the

• Impact of IDEA and ADA on the roles of student, teacher, and school	1	2	3
• Requirements and demands of college coursework	1	2	3
• Range of support services through Disability Support Services and other campus resources	1	2	3
• Your need for disability support in college and how to establish eligibility and access	1	2	3
• Vocabulary related to college and disability	1	2	3

Accessing Support from Adult Human Services Agencies

You can identify Adult Human Service agencies (e.g., Vocational Rehabilitation) that provide support services to individuals with disabilities enrolled in college and understand how to apply for these services.

You have identified

• Public and private agencies that provide support services to college students with disabilities	1	2	3
• Application procedures for these support services	1	2	3

Source: Planning Worksheet: Student Version. Retrieved January 25, 2008, from www.postitt.org/activities/TM_worksheets.pdf

Name _____   Date _____

Documenting My Disability

☼ **Please respond to each item to make sure you have all of the information you will need in the future.**

Does my current documentation include . . .

		Yes	No	NA
❶	A statement of my specific disability?.............................	❏	❏	❏
❷	Date of most recent evaluation?	❏	❏	❏
❸	Acceptable formal/informal assessment information?..............	❏	❏	❏
❹	Performance levels with and without accommodations?	❏	❏	❏
❺	Information on the current functional impact of my disability?......	❏	❏	❏
❻	Response to previous instructional interventions?..................	❏	❏	❏
❼	A history of previous accommodations?	❏	❏	❏
❽	Recommendations for accommodations and support services needed for success in postsecondary education?	❏	❏	❏
❾	Other information?			
	_____	❏	❏	❏
	_____	❏	❏	❏

Source: Disability Documentation Evaluation. Retrieved January 25, 2008, from www.postitt.org/activities/unit04/TM_disability_services.pdf

Class Formats and My Success

☼ **Describe how each format has contributed to your success or difficulty with classes in the past. Use this information to help you select future classes and instructors.**

Class Format	Contribute to My Success	Contribute to My Difficulties
Lectures		
Class discussions		
Reading textbooks		
Instruction on overhead or board		
Small-group work tasks		
Hands-on activities		
Daily written assignments		
Long-term projects		
Chapter/unit tests		
Timed tests or activities		

Source: Transition to Postsecondary Education: Strategies for Students with Disabilities (p. 27) by K. W. Webb, 2000, Austin, TX: PRO-ED. Copyright 2000 by PRO-ED, Inc. Adapted with permission.

Name _____   Date _____

My Challenges

☀ **Please complete each section.**

Dealing with Frustration

Put a ✔ *beside the statements that are true for you.*

_____   I get angry with my teachers when they can't help me figure something out.

_____   I get angry with my teachers when they expect me to know more than I do.

_____   I get angry with other learners when they make too much noise or get in my way when I am trying to pay attention.

_____   I get frustrated when I can't learn something, and I take it out on the teacher or other learners.

_____   I get angry with myself and give up.

_____   I get so upset when I earn a bad grade that I can't go on with the rest of the class.

◼ What do you do when you feel yourself beginning to get angry?

_____

_____

◼ Do you have any ideas about what might help you do better in these areas? Has something worked for you in the past?

_____

_____

◼ What have you tried that didn't work or didn't work well when you felt yourself getting angry?

_____

_____

◼ What else would you like your teachers to know?

_____

_____

Talking to Others

Put a ✔ *beside the statements that are true for you.*

_____   Other people often have a problem understanding what I say.

_____   I have a hard time figuring out what I want to say to the instructor. It doesn't come out right.

_____   I have a hard time asking for what I need.

_____   I don't raise my hand in class when I have a question because I can't get the words out correctly.

◼ Do you have a problem giving someone directions when they ask you for them? If so, what do you do when this happens?

_____

_____

➲

Source: I. A.A.M.: Ensuring Appropriate Accommodations for Students with Disabilities (pp. 20–24), by M. P. Gilbert, W. Dunn, K. Parker, G. Berry, N. Kurth, and D. Mellard, 2002, Lawrence: University of Kansas Center for Research on Learning, Division of Adult Studies. Copyright 2002 by University of Kansas. Adapted with permission.

◼ Is it hard for people to understand you on the phone? If yes, how do you help people understand you more clearly?

_____

_____

◼ Do you have any ideas about what might help you do a better job of talking to others? Has something worked for you in the past?

_____

_____

◼ What have you tried that didn't work or didn't work well when talking to others?

_____

_____

◼ What else about your speech would you like your teachers to know?

_____

_____

Hearing

Put a ✔ beside the statements that are true for you.

_____ I can't hear the instructor all the time.

_____ I can hear the instructor only if he or she sits or stands right in front of me or to one side.

_____ I can't hear the instructor with noise in the room.

_____ I can't hear other students when they ask questions or make comments.

_____ I can read lips.

_____ I use sign language. If yes, what kind? *(e.g. ASL, SEE, etc.)* _____

_____ I use a TDD, telecommunications device, or special telephone for the deaf.

◼ Has a doctor told you that you have a problem that keeps you from hearing as well as you should?

_____

_____

◼ Has your hearing stayed the same for some time, or has it become worse?

_____

_____

◼ Do you have a problem getting information from someone outside the classroom? If so, what do you do to get the information you need?

_____

_____

◼ Do you have a problem following what is going on at meetings or at the movies? If yes, how do you solve this problem?

_____

_____

Source: I. A.A.M.: Ensuring Appropriate Accommodations for Students with Disabilities (pp. 20–24), by M. P. Gilbert, W. Dunn, K. Parker, G. Berry, N. Kurth, and D. Mellard, 2002, Lawrence: University of Kansas Center for Research on Learning, Division of Adult Studies. Copyright 2002 by University of Kansas. Adapted with permission.

■ Do you have any ideas about what might help you do better in these areas? Has something worked for you in the past?

_____

_____

■ What have you tried that didn't work at all or didn't work well when trying to hear others?

_____

_____

■ What else about your hearing would you like your teachers to know?

_____

_____

_____

Sitting for Long Periods

Put a ✔ beside the statements that are true for you.

_____ I get very tired.

_____ I hurt or am uncomfortable.

_____ I get "antsy." I need to move around.

_____ I need to change positions to keep a sore from starting or getting worse.

■ I can stay still for _____ minutes/hours when I am doing school work. After that, I need to get up because

_____

_____

■ Is there anything that you do or know about that might help you in this area? If so, what is it?

_____

_____

■ What have you tried that didn't work at all or didn't work well when you had to sit for long periods?

_____

_____

■ What else about sitting for long periods would you like your teachers to know?

_____

_____

_____

Moving Around in the Classroom

Put a ✔ beside the statements that are true for you.

_____ I can't get myself to the classroom in my wheelchair.

_____ I can't get my wheelchair through the door of the classroom.

_____ I can't move my wheelchair around the room once inside.

_____ I can't walk all the way to the room.

_____ I can't see things in the way when I am walking.

_____ I can't reach all of the material and supplies that I need in lab courses.

Source: I. A.A.M.: Ensuring Appropriate Accommodations for Students with Disabilities (pp. 20–24), by M. P. Gilbert, W. Dunn, K. Parker, G. Berry, N. Kurth, and D. Mellard, 2002, Lawrence: University of Kansas Center for Research on Learning, Division of Adult Studies. Copyright 2002 by University of Kansas. Adapted with permission.

■ What have you done in the past when having a problem getting into or moving around a classroom or other room in a building?

_____

_____

■ What else about getting around would you like your teachers to know?

_____

_____

Moving or Manipulating Objects

Put a ✔ beside the statements that are true for you.

_____ I have difficulty turning the pages in a book.

_____ Writing utensils like pencils and pens are hard for me to grip and use.

_____ I have trouble picking up small objects like paperclips or coins.

_____ It's difficult for me to put a key in a lock and turn it.

_____ It's hard for me to push the buttons on a keyboard, touchtone phone, or calculator.

■ Is there anything that you do or know about that might help you be better able to move or manipulate objects?

_____

_____

■ What have you tried that didn't work at all or didn't work well when trying to manipulate objects?

_____

_____

■ What else about the way you move or manipulate objects would you like your teachers to know?

_____

_____

Source: I. A.A.M.: Ensuring Appropriate Accommodations for Students with Disabilities (pp. 20–24), by M. P. Gilbert, W. Dunn, K. Parker, G. Berry, N. Kurth, and D. Mellard, 2002, Lawrence: University of Kansas Center for Research on Learning, Division of Adult Studies. Copyright 2002 by University of Kansas. Adapted with permission.

Name _____   Date _____

My Learning and Living Strengths

☀ **Please respond to each statement.**

Classroom Activities

I can effectively . . .

	Yes	No
1. Listen to classroom lectures.	☐	☐
2. Listen to classroom discussions in various types and sizes of classrooms.	☐	☐
3. Participate in classroom discussions.	☐	☐
4. Participate in small discussion groups.	☐	☐
5. Answer questions raised in class or in discussion groups.	☐	☐
6. View information written on boards or on overhead projectors.	☐	☐
7. Hear and view films and videotape presentations.	☐	☐
8. Take notes using pen or pencil.	☐	☐
9. Use science laboratory equipment as part of a science lab.	☐	☐

★ List the support and adaptations that would help you complete these activities.

_____

_____

Studying

I can . . .

	Yes	No
1. Read standard print in publications such as textbooks, dictionaries, journals, newspapers.	☐	☐
2. Use pen or pencil to do math problems.	☐	☐
3. Use a standard calculator with standard-size keys.	☐	☐
4. Lift and replace books from library shelves.	☐	☐
5. Search for information on computer databases.	☐	☐

★ List the support and adaptations that would help you complete these activities.

_____

_____

➲

Source: Iowa Program for Assistive Technology. (n.d.). *Going to College?* Retrieved January 23, 2006, from www.uiowa.edu/infotech/college.htm
Adapted with permission.

Course Examinations

I can . . .

	Yes	No
1. Complete exams, using pen or pencil.	☐	☐
2. Complete exams using a computer.	☐	☐
3. Use a pencil to fill in circles on a computer-scored answer sheet.	☐	☐
4. Use laboratory equipment to complete or view items in a science laboratory examination.	☐	☐

★ List the support and adaptations that would help you complete these activities.

_____

_____

Use of Computers

I can . . .

	Yes	No
1. Use a computer with a standard keyboard.	☐	☐
2. See information on a standard computer screen.	☐	☐
3. Hear computer tones or signals of error.	☐	☐
4. Use a computer at a standard work station that has not been modified.	☐	☐

★ List the support and adaptations that would help you complete these activities.

_____

_____

Transportation

I can . . .

	Yes	No
1. Drive; I have access to a vehicle.	☐	☐
2. Use mass transit, including fixed-route bus systems or para-transit.	☐	☐
3. Travel on my own between campus buildings using an accessible route.	☐	☐

★ List the support and adaptations that would help you complete these activities.

_____

_____

Daily Living Skills

	Yes	No
1. I can complete the following personal-care skills independently.		
• Bathing	☐	☐
• Grooming	☐	☐
• Toileting	☐	☐
• Dressing	☐	☐
• Getting in and out of bed without assistance	☐	☐

Source: Iowa Program for Assistive Technology. (n.d.). *Going to College?* Retrieved January 23, 2006, from www.uiowa.edu/infotech/college.htm
Adapted with permission.

2. I can function in the following standard living environments that have not been modified.

	Yes	No
• Bathroom..	☐	☐
• Shower..	☐	☐
• Sink	☐	☐
• Bed..	☐	☐
• Desk...	☐	☐
• Closet	☐	☐
• Shelves...	☐	☐

3. I can . . .

	Yes	No
• Manipulate controls for light switches, radios, stereos, and other electronic devices.	☐	☐
• Use a standard telephone.	☐	☐
• Open doors using standard keys.	☐	☐
• Be alerted by standard fire alarm systems.	☐	☐

★ List the support and adaptations that would help you complete these activities.

_____

_____

_____

Leisure and Extracurricular Activities

1. I can use the following:

	Yes	No
• Electronic games...	☐	☐
• Stereo equipment..	☐	☐
• Television equipment	☐	☐
• Sports equipment..	☐	☐
• Photography equipment	☐	☐
• Camping and other outdoor equipment	☐	☐
• Fishing equipment..	☐	☐

	Yes	No
2. I can attend and participate in student organization meetings and events.	☐	☐
3. I can attend and participate in campus-wide programs.	☐	☐
4. I can attend programs, plays, and other events at the campus theater and auditorium..........	☐	☐

★ List the supports and adaptations that would help you complete these activities.

_____

_____

_____

Source: Iowa Program for Assistive Technology. (n.d.). *Going to College?* Retrieved January 23, 2006, from www.uiowa.edu/infotech/college.htm Adapted with permission.

Name _____   Date _____

Solving Problems

☀ **Select a problem that you are currently facing, and complete the process below.**

What is the problem?

Why is it a problem?

What have you done to solve it?

What else might help?

What do you have to do?

Do you have a system or a plan?

What do you see as the solution?

Source: Tools for Transition (p. 9), by American Guidance Service, Inc., 1991, Circle Pines, MN: Author. Copyright 1991 by AGS. Adapted with permission.

Name _____ Date _____

Self-Determination Planning

☼ **For each skill area, identify your needs, and list ideas for addressing these needs.**

Self-Determination Skill Areas	Identify Your Self-Determination Needs for Postsecondary Education	List Ideas About How to Address These Needs
Self-knowledge and self-awareness		
Choice making		
Problem solving		
Decision making		
Goal setting and attainment		
Risk taking and safety		
Self-regulation		
Self-advocacy or leadership		
Interpersonal communication		

Source: Preparing for Postsecondary Education and Training: Overview Information Strategies (p. 1), by K. B. Flannery, R. Slovic, M. C. Dalmau, S. Bigaj, and N. Hart, 2000, Eugene: University of Oregon. Copyright 2000 by University of Oregon. Adapted with permission

Planning for Postsecondary Education/Training: Preparing for My Future

List of Inventories

Student Name _____   Your Name _____

Grade _____ Age _____ Date _____   Your Role _____

Post-IEP Planning: Staff

☼ **Circle the number that indicates the student's current level of knowledge or ability in the areas listed.**

Rating Scale: 1 = *No knowledge or ability*
2 = *Some knowledge or ability*
3 = *High level of knowledge or ability*

Developing Knowledge and Skills To Be a Self-Advocate

The student understands his or her disability, learning strengths, and related accommodations and has the skills to self-advocate in the academic setting.

The student has identified

- His or her disability (What is it? How does it affect the student in the classroom?)........... 1 2 3
- Learning strengths (How does the student learn best?)................................... 1 2 3
- Appropriate accommodations based on disability and learning strengths 1 2 3
- How his/her disability documentation supports specific accommodations 1 2 3
- How to practice self-advocacy in the high school setting................................ 1 2 3

Assistive Technology

The student understands how assistive technology can effectively accommodate his/her limitations.

The student has an understanding of

- Assistive technology and how it can be used to accommodate learning 1 2 3
- How everyday items can be used as assistive technology................................ 1 2 3
- The assistive technology he/she currently uses 1 2 3
- Which high technologies can assist him/her in learning................................ 1 2 3

Planning

The student has established a realistic college education goal and has prepared a timeline for successful transition to college.

The student has identified

- Personal interests 1 2 3
- Possible career choices 1 2 3
- A college goal based on interests and strengths 1 2 3
- Academic courses required to meet college goal 1 2 3
- A high school timeline of college planning and application activities..................... 1 2 3

➡

Source: Planning Worksheet: Staff Version. Retrieved January 25, 2008, from www.postitt.org/activities/TM_worksheets.pdf

Applying to College

The student has finished the college admissions process from identifying appropriate college programs, completing admission criteria, completing financial aid applications, and providing appropriate disability documentation.

The student has identified

• Colleges that match interests with academic programs and support needs	1	2	3
• Admission requirements in colleges of interests	1	2	3
• Differences in support services among colleges	1	2	3

The student has completed

• Precollege admissions and/or placement testing (SAT, ACT, ASSET)	1	2	3
• Competitive college applications and supporting letters and essays	1	2	3
• Financial aid application	1	2	3
• Establishing eligibility for services by meeting with the Disability Support Services coordinator, once accepted at a college	1	2	3

Accessing Support on a College Campus

The student understands the changing roles and responsibilities for the student and school in the provision of disability-related support services in college.

The student has an understanding of the

• Impact of IDEA and ADA on the roles of student, teacher, and school	1	2	3
• Requirements and demands of college coursework	1	2	3
• Range of support services through Disability Support Services and other campus resources	1	2	3
• Differences in support services among colleges	1	2	3
• Need for disability support in college and how to establish eligibility and access	1	2	3
• Vocabulary related to college and disability	1	2	3

Accessing Support from Adult Human Services Agencies

The student can identify Adult Human Service agencies that provide support services to individuals with disabilities enrolled in college and understand how to apply for these services.

The student has identified

• Public and private agencies that provide support services to college students with disabilities	1	2	3
• Application procedures for these support services	1	2	3

Source: Planning Worksheet: Staff Version. Retrieved January 25, 2008, from www.postitt.org/activities/TM_worksheets.pdf

Name _____   Date _____

School _____   Year in School _____

Transition Calendar from High School

☼ **This is a list of steps to take during each year of high school. Put a check mark beside each item you complete.**

Freshman and Sophomore Years

☐ Explore career interests and potential life goals

☐ Take an interest inventory or vocational assessment

☐ Assess and work on improving study skills and habits

☐ Determine educational needs of possible careers

☐ Determine the high school courses required by colleges or vocational–technical centers

☐ Establish a file for high school and disability records

☐ Attend career information programs and fairs. Seek information from counselors, teachers, businesses, and family

Junior Year

☐ Start to firm up life goals and career choice

☐ Start to explore programs offered by colleges, community colleges, and vocational–technical centers

☐ Seek information from adult agencies, such as the Division of Vocational Rehabilitation, the Division of Blind Services, etc., regarding their services

☐ Apply, if eligible, for services from adult agencies

☐ Explore possible financial aid and scholarships

☐ Take the *Scholastic Aptitude Test* (SAT) or *American College Test* (ACT), if appropriate, in the spring (special accommodations can be arranged with either testing agency)

☐ Visit postsecondary schools

Senior Year

☐ Identify career choices and gather information on them

☐ Check deadlines for application and financial aid

☐ Visit colleges, community colleges, or vocational–technical centers

☐ Apply to school and for financial aid

☐ Request transcripts be sent to the college or vocational–technical center

☐ Participate in the completion of the Summary of Performance document

Source: Postsecondary Education Support Services: A Guide for Students with Disabilities, by Project RETAIN, 1994, Tallahassee: Florida Network. Copyright 1994 by Florida Network; Information and Services for Adolescents and Adults with Special Needs. Adapted with permission.

Name _____   Date _____

Trade, Technical, or Apprenticeship Programs

☼ To help you learn more about various trade, technical, or apprenticeship programs, interview program representatives or people who have completed the programs.

Trade, Technical, or Apprenticeship Program Options	High School Diploma Required		Program Length	Start Date	Special Opportunities for Diversity		Number of Graduates Employed Each Year
	Yes	No			Yes	No	
_____	☐	☐	_____	_____	☐	☐	_____
_____	☐	☐	_____	_____	☐	☐	_____
_____	☐	☐	_____	_____	☐	☐	_____
_____	☐	☐	_____	_____	☐	☐	_____
_____	☐	☐	_____	_____	☐	☐	_____
_____	☐	☐	_____	_____	☐	☐	_____
_____	☐	☐	_____	_____	☐	☐	_____
_____	☐	☐	_____	_____	☐	☐	_____
_____	☐	☐	_____	_____	☐	☐	_____
_____	☐	☐	_____	_____	☐	☐	_____

Source: Copyright 2008 by Gary M. Clark. Used with permission.

Name _____   Date _____

Training-in-the-Military Checklist

☼ **Circle Yes or No to answer the following questions.**

❶ I know how the military tests volunteers for aptitudes and interests. . . . .   **Yes**   **No**

❷ I know that the military cannot guarantee that I will be assigned to a technical area for which
I want to receive training. . . . .   **Yes**   **No**

❸ I know the differences between technical training in the military and technical training in
public or private schools. . . . .   **Yes**   **No**

❹ I know the options available through the military for taking college courses for credit. . . . .   **Yes**   **No**

❺ I know that there is a chance that military duty assignments will not match my interests
or aptitudes. . . . .   **Yes**   **No**

❻ I know how technical training in the military relates to a career within the military and certain
occupations in civilian life. . . . .   **Yes**   **No**

❼ I know that some psychological or medical evaluations will disqualify me for military service
and training in my area of interest. . . . .   **Yes**   **No**

❽ I know the military's policies on accommodations for disability. . . . .   **Yes**   **No**

❾ I know the military's policies on sexual identity/preference. . . . .   **Yes**   **No**

Source: Copyright 2008 by Gary M. Clark. Used with permission.

Name _____   Date _____

Exploring Military Training

☀ **Ask these questions during an interview with a military recruiter. Write the recruiter's answers or your notes in the space below each question.**

Recruiter's Name _____   Branch of the Military _____

1. Will this branch of military service accept someone with my disability?

_____

_____

_____

2. What is the minimum tour of duty or time commitment for your branch of the service?

_____

_____

_____

3. What kind of training will the military give me in my interest areas?

_____

_____

_____

4. Will my disability affect my ability to fulfill expectations in the military? Will there be ways for the military to accommodate difficulties associated with my disability?

_____

_____

_____

5. How do military training and work opportunities compare with civilian training and work opportunities I might have?

_____

_____

_____

Source: Tools for Transition: Student Handbook (p. 31), by E. P. Aune and J. E. Ness, 1991, Circle Pines, MN: American Guidance Service. Copyright 1991 by American Guidance Service. Adapted with permission.

Name _____   Date _____

Before-Going-to-College Checklist

☀ **Put a check mark in the box beside each step you have completed.**

☐ I am taking high school courses that will get me into college.

☐ I am attending my Individualized Education Program (IEP) meetings.

☐ I have discussed all assessment information with my school psychologist, counselor, special education teacher, and parents.

☐ I know my academic and personal strengths and weaknesses.

☐ I can describe my disability in detail.

☐ I know the kinds of accommodations that will provide me with an equal opportunity to succeed at college.

☐ I have had meetings with a high school special education teacher and a guidance staff member and discussed what I need to do to prepare for college.

☐ I have participated in the development of my Summary of Performance document.

☐ I have taken the *Scholastic Aptitude Test* (SAT) or the *American College Testing Program* (ACT).

☐ I have sufficient reading and writing skills to handle the demands of college classes.

☐ I have sufficient study skills for college-level work.

☐ I am taking on more difficult tasks without the help of my teachers or parents.

☐ I have located colleges that have disability resource centers and programs for students with disabilities.

☐ I have reviewed their course catalogs.

☐ I have visited the colleges I would like to attend, seen the campuses, and met with the disability resource center staff.

Source: Transitions To Postsecondary Learning: Self-Advocacy Handbook for Students with Learning Disabilities and/or Attention Deficit Disorder (p. 64), by H. Eaton and L. Coull, 1998, Vancouver, BC, Canada: Eaton Coull Learning Group. Copyright 1998 by Eaton Coull Learning Group. Adapted with permission.

Name _____ Date _____

High School-to-College Checklist

☀ **Put a check mark in the Yes or No column to indicate if each statement matches you.**

		Yes	No
1.	I take the most academically challenging courses possible.	❑	❑
2.	I consult my teachers on how to become an independent learner.	❑	❑
3.	I actively participate in my IEP meetings by suggesting goals and needed supports.	❑	❑
4.	I look for opportunities to become more independent at home and in school.	❑	❑
5.	I expand my career interests through electives and extracurricular activities.	❑	❑
6.	I have identified my preferences and interests for the future.	❑	❑
7.	I have a good understanding of my disability(ies).	❑	❑
8.	I know my rights for educational accommodations in high school and college.	❑	❑
9.	My grades so far put me on track for graduation and college admission.	❑	❑
10.	I have taken a college admission exam and begun the college selection process.	❑	❑
11.	I have talked to a counselor about what I need to be able to receive accommodations and supports in college.	❑	❑
12.	I have developed a financial plan for my estimated college expenses.	❑	❑
13.	I have narrowed my selection to at least three colleges and made application to each.	❑	❑
14.	I have visited, when possible, the campuses of the colleges in which I am interested.	❑	❑
15.	I have actively participated in the development of my Summary of Performance document.	❑	❑

Source: Copyright 2008 by Patricia L. Sitlington. Used with permission. .

Name _____   Date _____

College-Decision Question List

☼ **Use this list as a guide when you visit schools to assist you with making a final decision.**

Factor	Questions to Consider	My Thoughts About This School
Location	• How near or far from home/support system would you like to be when attending college?	
Size of College	• Would you prefer to attend a school with a large enrollment (30,000+ students), a small one (1,500), or something in the middle? • How large would you like the physical size of the campus to be?	
Environment	• Would you rather attend a community college or a 4-year university? • Would you rather attend an urban, a suburban, or a rural school? • Is the location and size of the nearest city important to you? • Do you prefer a coed or same sex dorm? • Does the school's religious affiliation make a difference to you?	
Admission Requirements	• For which colleges/universities do your GPA, class rank, or ACT/SAT scores meet admission criteria?	
Academics	• Which schools offer the major(s) your are considering? • What kind of student–faculty ratio are you looking for? • Does the college offer special services and programs that take into account your needs? • If you require tutoring, is it available? What will it cost?	
College Expenses	• How expensive of a school can you afford? (Be sure to consider tuition, room and board, deposits, and other expenses.)	
Financial Aid	• Does the school offer additional assistance outside of federal and state student aid?	
Housing	• Will you live on campus in a dorm or commute to school? • If you commute, where will you live, and how will you get to school?	
Facilities	• What type of academic and recreational facilities would you like the college to have?	
Activities	• What kinds of clubs and organizations do you want your college to offer? • With what type of activities (including intramural teams) would you like to get involved with?	

Source: Transition Information Packet: TIP (pp. 27–28), by Iowa Department of Human Services Transition Planning Specialists, 2002, Des Moines: Iowa Department of Human Services. Adapted with permission.

Name _____ Date _____

School Analysis

☼ **Use this form to help you organize information about a school you are considering.**

Your Career Goal _____

School _____

Location _____ Cost _____

Your Educational/Career Goals _____

Application Deadlines for Financial Aid _____

Application Deadlines for Admissions _____

  1. **a.** Does the school offer programs related to your educational and career goals?

   b. How long is the program? _____

   c. Will additional schooling or training be necessary? _____

  2. How many students attend the school? _____

  3. What is the average class size for freshmen? _____

  4. What is the quality of the academic facilities? _____

  5. Are job placement services available? _____

  6. **a.** What types of financial aid are available? _____

   b. From what sources? _____

   c. What application forms do you need to complete? _____

  7. Describe the living facilities. _____
   _____

  8. Describe the social/recreational facilities. _____
   _____

  9. **a.** Do you know anyone who has attended this school? _____

   b. What is his or her opinion of it? _____

  10. What does your high school counselor say about this school? _____

  11. What do college resource guides say about this school? _____
   _____
   _____

Source: School Comparison Worksheet (p. 10), by National Association of Student Financial Aid Administrators, 2004, Washington, DC: Author. Copyright 2004 by National Association of Student Aid Administrators. Adapted with permission.

Name _____   Date _____

College Planning List

☀ **Identify when each activity should be accomplished, and keep track of when you do it.**

Junior Year

Task To Be Completed	Deadline	Date Completed	Notes
▣ Meet with college counselor	_____	_____	_____
▣ Register for the PSAT	_____	_____	_____
▣ Meet with college representatives who visit your school	_____	_____	_____
▣ Take the PSAT	_____	_____	_____
▣ Review PSAT/NMSQT scores	_____	_____	_____
▣ Register for the spring ACT (or other tests)	_____	_____	_____
▣ Register for the spring SAT	_____	_____	_____
▣ Register for the May/June SAT (if appropriate)	_____	_____	_____
▣ Take the spring ACT	_____	_____	_____
▣ Begin receiving mail from colleges	_____	_____	_____
▣ Take the spring SAT	_____	_____	_____
▣ Request college applications	_____	_____	_____
▣ Take the May/June SAT (if appropriate)	_____	_____	_____
▣ Plan to visit college campuses	_____	_____	_____

➲

Source: College Planning Checklist (pp. 1–4), by National Research Center for College and University Admissions, n.d., Lee's Summit, MO: Author. Copyright by National Research Center for College and University Admissions. Adapted with permission.

Senior Year

Task To Be Completed	Deadline	Date Completed	Notes
▣ Review your list of top colleges with your counselor	_____	_____	_____
▣ Request financial aid forms, the college Scholarship Service's PROFILE, and the FAFSA	_____	_____	_____
▣ Submit enrollment deposit	_____	_____	_____

My Top 10 Colleges and Universities

1. _____
2. _____
3. _____
4. _____
5. _____

6. _____
7. _____
8. _____
9. _____
10. _____

Check off each task as completed

	1	2	3	4	5	6	7	8	9	10
Application received										
Application deadline										
Campus visit										
Request counselor & teacher recommendations										
Write essay										
Request transcripts										
Request first semester grades										
Financial aid forms submitted										
Scholarship forms submitted										
Other _____										
Other _____										

Source: College Planning Checklist (pp. 1–4), by National Research Center for College and University Admissions, n.d., Lee's Summit, MO: Author. Copyright by National Research Center for College and University Admissions. Adapted with permission.

Name _____   Date _____

College Accessibility/Services: Visual Impairment

☀ **Check out whether the following services are available.**

Yes	No	
☐	☐	Does the college offer mobility orientation and training for the campus?
☐	☐	If so, does the college have a list of qualified instructors?
☐	☐	Does the college have volunteer readers?
☐	☐	If not, does the college provide paid readers?
☐	☐	Does the college help me find readers?
☐	☐	Will the college provide access to technology for readings/texts?
☐	☐	Are large-print computer programs available to me?
☐	☐	Are voice-activated computer programs available to me?
☐	☐	Will the college provide accommodations for exams?
☐	☐	Is special campus transportation available to me?
☐	☐	Is there community transportation available to me?

Source: Complete Guide to Special Education Transition Services (p. 160), by R. Pierangelo, 1997, Hoboken, NJ: Wiley. Copyright 1997 by John Wiley & Sons. Adapted with Permission.

College Accessibility/Services: Hearing Impairment

☼ **Check out whether the following services are available.**

Yes	No	
☐	☐	Will the college provide qualified interpreters?
☐	☐	Will I be able to have an interpreter with my preferred manual system?
☐	☐	Are oral interpreters available to me?
☐	☐	Is live captioning available to me for live speakers?
☐	☐	Are note takers available to record lectures for me?
☐	☐	If so, do I have to find my own note takers?
☐	☐	Does the campus have TDDs in campus buildings and dormitories?
☐	☐	Do dormitory telephones have volume control?
☐	☐	Do the dormitories have visual alarm systems in case of fire or emergencies?
☐	☐	Is amplification equipment available in performance arts areas?

Source: Complete Guide to Special Education Transition Services (p. 161), by R. Pierangelo, 1997, Hoboken, NJ: Wiley. Copyright 1997 by John Wiley & Sons. Adapted with Permission.

Name _____   Date _____

College Accessibility/Services: Mobility Impairment

☀ **Check out whether the following services are available.**

Yes	No	
☐	☐	Is there full accessibility to all campus buildings and facilities?
☐	☐	Will the college provide transportation on campus?
☐	☐	Will the college assist me in scheduling classes to permit travel time?
☐	☐	Will the college provide special adaptations to computers at the library or in computer labs?
☐	☐	Is wheelchair repair available on campus or in the community?
☐	☐	Is there a list of approved personal attendants?
☐	☐	Is driver evaluation and training available?

Source: Complete Guide to Special Education Transition Services (p. 161), by R. Pierangelo, 1997, Hoboken, NJ: Wiley. Copyright 1997 by John Wiley & Sons. Adapted with Permission.

College Information

☀ **Find out the information for each of the following areas.**

Name of College _____

1. What are admission requirements?

   _____

2. What is the required grade point average, ACT, or SAT score?

   _____

3. Are there special accommodations for individuals with disabilities to take entrance exams?

   _____

4. Are there special incentive programs?

   _____

5. Is there a disabled student service office on campus? How does one contact the office? Is there a Web site? Does it have a full-time person, or part time?

   _____

6. What kind of documentation is required to verify disabilities?

   _____

7. Is there an organization for students with disabilities on campus? How does one contact them?

   _____

8. How are the course instructors informed of the necessary accommodations, if needed?

   _____

9. Is tutoring available? Is it individualized, or group? Is there a cost involved?

   _____

10. Are note takers and readers available? Is there a cost involved? How are they trained?

    _____

11. Is it possible to arrange for tape-recorded classes, computers, untimed testing, and test readers?

    _____

12. Is it possible to relocate classes to more accessible sites?

    _____

13. What is the college's policy regarding course substitutes or waiver of curriculum requirements?

    _____

14. Are there developmental courses available? In what areas?

    _____

Source: *Complete Guide to Special Education Transition Services* (p. 159), by R. Pierangelo, 1997, Hoboken, NJ: Wiley. Copyright 1997 by John Wiley & Sons. Adapted with Permission.

Name _____ Date _____

Learning Support Services and Programs

☼ **Check out the nature and types of services available at the school you are considering.**

	YES	NO
1. Does the program have a full-time disability director?...	❏	❏
2. Does the program have a disability assistant coordinator?.......................................	❏	❏
3. Does the program provide a full range of accommodations?	❏	❏
4. Does each student in the program have an "Individualized Semester Plan"?.....................	❏	❏
5. Is tutoring available from staff and graduate-level interns who are trained in disabilities?	❏	❏
6. Does the program have a full-time disability coordinator?.......................................	❏	❏
7. Are the services housed in the disability student services office?................................	❏	❏
8. Are accommodations provided for testing and coursework?	❏	❏
9. Are there established policies on admissions and service delivery?..............................	❏	❏
10. Is there a strong emphasis on student self-advocacy?...	❏	❏
11. Are student support groups available?	❏	❏
12. Are specially trained tutors available?	❏	❏
13. Are students required to provide documentation of their disabilities?...........................	❏	❏
14. Are services available all year, including summer-school sessions?..............................	❏	❏
15. Does the service have a contact person?	❏	❏
16. Are generic support services available (e.g., taped textbooks, readers, note takers, alternate test administration)?	❏	❏
17. Are peer tutors available to students who are at risk?...	❏	❏
18. Are students referred to other on-campus resources?..	❏	❏
19. Are services provided without an official contact person?	❏	❏
20. Are services for students with disabilities limited?..	❏	❏
21. Does the program function with few established policies?	❏	❏
22. Are students dependent on building relationships with sympathetic faculty?	❏	❏
23. Does the college or university meet minimal requirements under Section 504 of the Rehabilitation Act?	❏	❏
24. How long has the program been in existence?	❏	❏
25. Are there fees for services to students with disabilities?	❏	❏
26. How many students with disabilities are registered with the program?...........................	❏	❏
27. How often does the average student use the program?	❏	❏
28. Could the director or assistant director attend the IEP meeting during the senior year?	❏	❏

Source: Resource Guide for Students with Learning Disabilities in Connecticut Colleges and Universities (1989; revised 1996, 1999), by J. M. McGuire and S. F. Shaw (Eds.), Storrs: University of Connecticut, Neag School of Education. Copyright 1989 by University of Connecticut. Adapted with permission.

Name _____   Date _____

College _____

Postsecondary Education Support Services

☀ **Keep track of the following important information.**

Office of Disability Support Services

- ◼ Name of person contacted _____

- ◼ Phone number _____

- ◼ What is the current system of support?

  _____ *Contact person* supports include _____

  _____

  _____

  _____ *As-needed* basic supports include _____

  _____

  _____

  _____ Comprehensive program providing consistent support includes _____

  _____

  _____

- ◼ What documentation is required, and how recent does it need to be? _____

  _____

  _____

- ◼ What services are available?

  _____ LD specialist   _____ Tutoring   _____ Group study sessions   _____ Peer support groups

  _____ Computer labs   _____ Agency referrals   _____ Other _____

- ◼ What curricular program modifications are available?

  _____ Language waivers   _____ Math waivers   _____ Other _____

- ◼ What course accommodations are available?

  _____ Untimed tests   _____ Oral tests   _____ Test readers   _____ Extended time for readings

  _____ Remedial work   _____ Note takers   _____ Course assignments   _____ Books on tape

  _____ Early access to syllabi   _____ Lectures on tape   _____ Other _____

- ◼ How many service providers are there? _____ ➡

Source: Unlocking Potential: College and Other Choices for People with LD and AD/HD (pp. 185–187), by J. M. Taymans, L. L. West, and M. Sullivan (Eds.), 2000, Bethesda, MD: Woodbine House. Copyright 2000 by J. M. Taymans, L. L. West, B. Scheiber, and J. Talpers. Adapted with permission.

Academic Support Resource Center

- ◼ Name of person contacted _____

- ◼ Phone number _____

- ◼ What is the current system of support?

  _____ *As-needed* basic supports include _____

  _____

  _____

  _____ Comprehensive program providing consistent support includes _____

  _____

  _____

- ◼ What types of counseling are available?

  _____ Academic counseling   _____ Study-skills instruction   _____ Career counseling   _____ Tutoring

- ◼ Is there a limit to the number of visits allotted? _____

- ◼ Does it cost additional money? _____

- ◼ How many professionals are there? _____

- ◼ Are there work programs established within the community?

  _____ Job placement   _____ Internship programs   _____ School credit

Counseling Center

- ◼ Name of person contacted _____

- ◼ Phone number _____

- ◼ What is the current system of support?

  _____ *As-needed* basic supports include _____

  _____

  _____

  _____ Comprehensive program providing consistent support includes _____

  _____

  _____

Source: *Unlocking Potential: College and Other Choices for People with LD and AD/HD* (pp. 185–187), by J. M. Taymans, L. L. West, and M. Sullivan (Eds.), 2000, Bethesda, MD: Woodbine House. Copyright 2000 by J. M. Taymans, L. L. West, B. Scheiber, and J. Talpers. Adapted with permission.

- What types of counseling are available?

  _____ Academic counseling _____ Career counseling _____ Personal counseling

- What documentation needs to be provided? ______________________________

  ____

  ____

- Is there group counseling? ______________________________

  Does it cost additional money? ______________________________

- Is there individual counseling? ______________________________

  Does it cost additional money? ______________________________

- Is there a limit to the number of visits allotted?______________________________

- How many professionals are there? ______________________________

Source: Unlocking Potential: College and Other Choices for People with LD and AD/HD (pp. 185–187), by J. M. Taymans, L. L. West, and M. Sullivan (Eds.), 2000, Bethesda, MD: Woodbine House. Copyright 2000 by J. M. Taymans, L. L. West, B. Scheiber, and J. Talpers. Adapted with permission.

© 2008 by PRO-ED, Inc.

Thinking About Education and Training Options

☼ **Use this activity to help you link your career goals with the program of study that will prepare you for this career.**

Career Goals

1 What career do you currently plan to pursue?

_____

2 What type of education does this career require?

_____

3 For what type of employer do you see yourself working when you complete your program?

_____

4 Where do you see yourself working when you complete your program?

_____

Education Goals

1 What types of schools offer programs in this area?

_____

2 List three schools that offer programs of study in this area of interest.

_____ (dream school—possibly difficult to be admitted)

_____ (school into which you should be accepted)

_____ (school into which you should have no problem being admitted)

Preparation Considerations

❶ Which prerequisite courses do I need to take in high school to pursue the program of studies for which I am interested?

_____

❷ Have I achieved grades that will allow me to be admitted into the schools I am interested in attending?

_____

❸ Have I achieved a class ranking that will allow me to be admitted into the schools I am interested in attending?

_____

❹ Are there any entry-requirement tests I need to take for the schools to which I am applying?

   ____ SAT   projected dates: _____

   ____ ACT   projected dates: _____

   ____ advanced placement   projected dates: _____

❺ Community service activities in which I have been involved:

_____

_____

_____

Name _____   Date _____

Evaluation of Final College Choices

☀ **Rate your final college choices on each of the characteristics shown.**

4 = *Excellent match with my interests and needs*
3 = *Good match with my interests and needs*
2 = *Fair match with my interests and needs*
1 = *Poor match with my interests and needs*

College Components	College Name _____	College Name _____	College Name _____
▣ Programs for students with disabilities	_____	_____	_____
▣ Other support resources (e.g., computer labs, library)	_____	_____	_____
▣ Cost of college tuition, books, housing, other expenses	_____	_____	_____
▣ Location of college	_____	_____	_____
▣ College climate	_____	_____	_____
▣ Overall strength of academic program	_____	_____	_____
▣ Strength of program in my career choice	_____	_____	_____
▣ Housing	_____	_____	_____
▣ My desire to attend this college	_____	_____	_____
Total	☐	☐	☐

Source: Transition to Postsecondary Education: Strategies for Students with Disabilities (p. 157), by K. W. Webb, 2000, Austin, TX: PRO-ED. Copyright 2000 by PRO-ED, Inc. Adapted with permission.

Academic Skills & Support Needs: Addressing Learning-Related Demands

List of Inventories

Study-Skills Checklist

☼ **Read each statement and consider how it applies to you. If it does apply to you, circle Y for Yes. If it does not apply to you, circle N for No.**

1. I spend too much time studying for what I am learning.	Y	N
2. I usually spend hours cramming the night before an exam.	Y	N
3. If I spend as much time on my social activities as I want to, I don't have enough time left to study, or when I study enough, I don't have time for a social life.	Y	N
4. I usually try to study with the radio and TV turned on.	Y	N
5. I can't sit and study for long periods of time without becoming tired or distracted.	Y	N
6. I go to class, but I usually doodle, daydream, or fall asleep.	Y	N
7. My class notes are sometimes difficult to understand later.	Y	N
8. I usually seem to get the wrong material into my class notes.	Y	N
9. I don't review my class notes periodically throughout the semester in preparation for tests.	Y	N
10. When I get to the end of a chapter, I can't remember what I've just read.	Y	N
11. I don't know how to pick out what is important in the text.	Y	N
12. I can't keep up with my reading assignments, and then I have to cram the night before a test.	Y	N
13. I lose a lot of points on essay tests, even when I know the material well.	Y	N
14. I study enough for my test, but when I get there, my mind goes blank.	Y	N
15. I often study in a haphazard, disorganized way under the threat of the next test.	Y	N
16. I often find myself getting lost in the details of reading and have trouble identifying the main ideas.	Y	N
17. I rarely change my reading speed in response to the difficulty level of the selection or my familiarity with the content.	Y	N
18. I often wish that I could read faster.	Y	N
19. When my teachers assign papers, I feel so overwhelmed that I can't get started.	Y	N
20. I usually write my papers the night before they are due.	Y	N
21. I can't seem to organize my thoughts into a paper that makes sense.	Y	N

☼ **Count the number of *Ys* you circled for each category.**

Category	Items	#Yes
Time Scheduling	1, 2, and 3	_____
Concentration	4, 5, and 6	_____
Listening & Note taking	7, 8, and 9	_____
Reading	10, 11, and 12	_____
Exams	13, 14, and 15	_____
Reading	16, 17, and 18	_____
Writing Skills	19, 20, and 21	_____

Source: Study Skills Checklist. Retrieved January 19, 2006, from www.lcc.vt.edu. Adapted with permission.

Name _____   Date _____

Study-Skills Questionnaire

☀ **Answer each question by placing a ✓ in the Yes or No column.**

Time Management

		YES	NO
1.	Do you usually have a well-organized study schedule?	☐	☐
2.	Do you see yourself as someone who uses his or her time effectively?	☐	☐
3.	Do you study for 1 or 2 hours per day with full concentration?	☐	☐
4.	Do you usually allow enough time for long-term assignments (e.g., term papers, lengthy reading assignments)?	☐	☐
5.	Do you finish your work far enough ahead of time to be able to proofread and make corrections?	☐	☐
6.	Do you accurately estimate how long it will take you to get work done?	☐	☐
7.	Do you hand in assignments late or ask for extensions?	☐	☐

Note Taking

		YES	NO
1.	Do you understand the notes you have taken in class?	☐	☐
2.	Do you feel that you can study from your notes (even if the test is 2 months later)?	☐	☐
3.	Do you share or compare notes with other students in the class?	☐	☐
4.	Are your notes legible?	☐	☐
5.	Have you ever used a tape recorder to supplement your notes?	☐	☐
6.	Do you date all your notes and class handouts?	☐	☐
7.	Are you able to keep up with all important information while the teacher is lecturing?	☐	☐
8.	Is it easy for you to select what information is important while you take notes?	☐	☐

Reading Assignments

		YES	NO
1.	Do you preview or survey your reading material and ask yourself questions before reading (do you establish a purpose for your reading)?	☐	☐
2.	Do you usually know the main ideas expressed in a reading assignment?	☐	☐
3.	Do you make a plan to divide a lengthy reading assignment into sections?	☐	☐
4.	After completing a reading assignment, do you review the lesson to organize what you have learned?	☐	☐
5.	Do you highlight or take notes when your read?	☐	☐
6.	Do you use the dictionary when you come across unfamiliar words?	☐	☐
7.	Do you use charts and graphs to aid your understanding when you read?	☐	☐

➡

Source: "Postsecondary Education," by G. DuChossois and C. A. Michaels, 1994, in *Transition Strategies for Persons with Learning Disabilities* (pp. 98–100), by C. A. Michaels (Ed.), Pacific Grove, CA: Delmar. Adapted with permission.

		YES	NO

8. Do you use the overall structure of the textbook to help you approach reading assignments (e.g., table of contents, glossary, headings and subheadings)?............................ ☐ ☐

9. Can you concentrate on and comprehend material on topics that you do not find interesting? ☐ ☐

Writing Assignments/Essays/Research Papers

1. Do you tend to have trouble thinking of words to express your ideas?..................... ☐ ☐

2. Is it harder for you to write as much as other students in your classes?.................... ☐ ☐

3. Does it take you a lot longer to write than you think it should?......................... ☐ ☐

4. Do you develop an outline for lengthier writing assignments before you start to write? .... ☐ ☐

5. Can you write in clear sentences?... ☐ ☐

6. Do readers find your writing well-organized and logical? .... ☐ ☐

7. Do you have trouble with spelling? .... ☐ ☐

8. Do you approach writing in stages, first completing a rough draft and then refining your work? .... ☐ ☐

9. Can you proofread your own work and find your errors? .... ☐ ☐

10. Do you use a word processor or computer with a spellcheck?........................... ☐ ☐

11. Do you ask others to read your reports and make suggestions? .... ☐ ☐

12. Can you use the library effectively to do research and gather information?................ ☐ ☐

13. Can you write a paper of a particular length?... ☐ ☐

14. Are the topics you choose appropriate to the assignment length (not too broad, not too narrow)?.. ☐ ☐

Examination Preparation

1. Do you find that you have studied the right information for tests?....................... ☐ ☐

2. Do you have strategies for memorizing material for exams?............................ ☐ ☐

3. Do you feel prepared for most tests?... ☐ ☐

4. Can you anticipate what questions might be on an exam?.............................. ☐ ☐

5. Do you prepare answers to possible essay questions before an exam?................... ☐ ☐

6. Do you study with other students in your class? .... ☐ ☐

7. Do you retain what you have studied when you get to the test?......................... ☐ ☐

8. Do you usually begin studying well in advance, or do you cram for exams? .... ☐ ☐

Test–Taking Behavior

1. Are you ready for exams (e.g., get there early, know the right time and date, have pens or pencils, have calculators)?.. ☐ ☐

2. Do you plan your exam time well (e.g., allow enough time for each section, know the point value of various questions, spend as much time on the end of a test as on the beginning)? ☐ ☐

Source: "Postsecondary Education," by G. DuChossois and C. A. Michaels, 1994, in *Transition Strategies for Persons with Learning Disabilities* (pp. 98–100), by C. A. Michaels (Ed.), Pacific Grove, CA: Delmar. Adapted with permission.

3. Do you usually have enough time to check your work (e.g., content, grammar, punctuation, calculations)?.. ☐ ☐

4. Do you have strategies for dealing with complex questions (e.g., underlining key words, narrowing down multiple-choice options)?... ☐ ☐

5. Do you accurately read test questions and directions?................................... ☐ ☐

6. Does test anxiety interfere with your performance on exams?........................... ☐ ☐

7. Is your sense of how well you performed on an exam usually accurate?.................. ☐ ☐

General Questions About You

1. Do you usually recognize when you need help, and are you willing to ask for it? .... ☐ ☐

2. Do you study in a place where you can concentrate? .... ☐ ☐

3. Do you have a routine time to study and do work (a time of day when you are most productive)?.. ☐ ☐

4. Do you pace yourself well when studying (e.g., take reasonable breaks, get back to work after breaks)?.. ☐ ☐

5. Are you able to make decisions about what you have to study? .... ☐ ☐

6. Can you set priorities?... ☐ ☐

7. Would your study habits enable you to be ready for a surprise quiz?...................... ☐ ☐

8. Do you monitor your own comprehension (i.e., do you stop yourself when you are not understanding material)? .... ☐ ☐

9. Can you comfortably describe your learning style or disability to others?.................. ☐ ☐

10. Can you identify strategies that help you learn (e.g., books on tape, one-to-one tutoring, study groups, rereading material, using a study guide)?................................. ☐ ☐

11. Do you get extra help each week? .... ☐ ☐

12. Do you prefer small discussion classes to large lecture classes?.......................... ☐ ☐

13. Do you feel that you are aware of what extra help and accommodations you need?........ ☐ ☐

14. Are you easily distracted? .... ☐ ☐

Source: "Postsecondary Education," by G. DuChossois and C. A. Michaels, 1994, in *Transition Strategies for Persons with Learning Disabilities* (pp. 98–100), by C. A. Michaels (Ed.), Pacific Grove, CA: Delmar. Adapted with permission.

Name _____   Date _____

Understanding How You Learn

☀ Use the "You" column to rate yourself on the following information. Ask your parent and your teacher to fill in the two columns on the right. Use the numbers 1, 2, 3, 4, or 5 to rate each trait: 1 is an area that is very difficult for you, and 5 is an area that is a strength for you. Compare the responses.

	You	Parent	Teacher
Learning Styles			
Learn best by seeing	____	____	____
Learn best by hearing	____	____	____
Learn best by doing	____	____	____
Learn best by touching	____	____	____
Academic Areas			
Reading speed	____	____	____
Reading comprehension	____	____	____
Main idea identification	____	____	____
Vocabulary	____	____	____
Writing	____	____	____
Creativity in writing	____	____	____
Word recall	____	____	____
Punctuation	____	____	____
Spelling	____	____	____
Understand math concepts	____	____	____
Math computation	____	____	____
Science	____	____	____
History	____	____	____
Literature	____	____	____
General working speed	____	____	____
Study Skills			
Legible notes	____	____	____
Meaningful notes	____	____	____
Complete notes	____	____	____
Highlighting	____	____	____
Use dictionary	____	____	____

Source: *Your Plan for Success: A College Preparation Manual for Students with Learning Disabilities* (pp. 22–25) by K. W. Webb, 1995, Freeport, IL: Peekan Publications. Copyright 1995 by Peekan Publications. Adapted with permission.

	You	Parent	Teacher
Know what to study	_____	_____	_____
Know when you need help	_____	_____	_____
Maintain focus *(not easily distracted)*	_____	_____	_____
Research skills	_____	_____	_____
Proofreading skills	_____	_____	_____

Organization

	You	Parent	Teacher
Time management	_____	_____	_____
Completion of assignments	_____	_____	_____
Completion of assignments on time	_____	_____	_____
Test-taking skills	_____	_____	_____
Commitment to study	_____	_____	_____
Keep track of assignments and tests	_____	_____	_____
Work independently	_____	_____	_____
Set goals	_____	_____	_____
Set priorities	_____	_____	_____
Organize material	_____	_____	_____
Memorize material	_____	_____	_____
Allow time to proofread	_____	_____	_____
Retrain information	_____	_____	_____
On time for class	_____	_____	_____
Keep appointments	_____	_____	_____

Social Skills

	You	Parent	Teacher
Understand nonverbal communication	_____	_____	_____
Understand humor	_____	_____	_____
Make appropriate small talk	_____	_____	_____
Express needs appropriately	_____	_____	_____
Relationships with peers	_____	_____	_____
Relationships with family	_____	_____	_____
Relationships with coworkers	_____	_____	_____
Relationships with teachers	_____	_____	_____
Listen as others talk	_____	_____	_____
Contribute to conversation	_____	_____	_____
Have clear value system	_____	_____	_____
Handle new situations	_____	_____	_____
Show leadership qualities	_____	_____	_____

Source: Your Plan for Success: A College Preparation Manual for Students with Learning Disabilities (pp. 22–25) by K. W. Webb, 1995, Freeport, IL: Peekan Publications. Copyright 1995 by Peekan Publications. Adapted with permission.

	You	Parent	Teacher
Think before acting	_____	_____	_____
On time for appointments	_____	_____	_____
Attend school regularly	_____	_____	_____
Sensitive to others' moods	_____	_____	_____
Obey class rules	_____	_____	_____
Respect others' property	_____	_____	_____
Avoid fights	_____	_____	_____
Respect Authority	_____	_____	_____
Positive feelings about self	_____	_____	_____
Accept criticism	_____	_____	_____
Tolerate frustration	_____	_____	_____

Others

	You	Parent	Teacher
_____	____	____	____
_____	____	____	____
_____	____	____	____
_____	____	____	____
_____	____	____	____
_____	____	____	____

Source: Your Plan for Success: A College Preparation Manual for Students with Learning Disabilities (pp. 22–25) by K. W. Webb, 1995, Freeport, IL: Peekan Publications. Copyright 1995 by Peekan Publications. Adapted with permission.

Student Name _____   Date _____

Person Completing Form _____

Learning-Needs Checklist

☀ **Put a ✓ by the statements that reflect your learning needs.**

❶ Reading Skills

☐ Slow reading rate and/or difficulty in modifying reading rate in accordance with the material's level of difficulty

☐ Uneven comprehension and retention of materials read

☐ Difficulty identifying important points and themes

☐ Incomplete mastery of phonics, confusion of similar words, difficulty integrating new vocabulary

☐ Skips words or lines of printed material

☐ Difficulty reading for long periods

❷ Written Language Skills

☐ Difficulty planning a topic and organizing thoughts on paper

☐ Difficulty with sentence structure (e.g., incomplete sentences, run-ons, poor use of grammar, missing inflectional endings)

☐ Frequent spelling errors (e.g., omissions, substitutions, transpositions), especially in specialized and foreign vocabulary

☐ Difficulty proofreading written work and making revisions

☐ Compositions are often limited in length

☐ Slow written production

☐ Poor penmanship (e.g., poorly formed letters, incorrect use of capitalization, trouble with spacing, overly large handwriting)

☐ Inability to copy correctly from a book or the blackboard

❸ Oral Language Skills

☐ Inability to concentrate on and to comprehend spoken language when presented rapidly

☐ Difficulty in orally expressing concepts that seem to be understood by others

☐ Difficulty following or having a conversation about an unfamiliar idea

☐ Trouble telling a story in the proper sequence

☐ Difficulty following oral or written directions

➜

Source: Unlocking Potential: College and Other Choices for People with LD and ADHD (pp. 264–265), by J. M. Taymans, L. L. West, and M. Sullivan (Eds.), 2000, Bethesda, MD: Woodbine House. Copyright 2000 by J. M. Taymans, L. L. West, and M. Sullivan. Adapted with permission.

❹ Mathematical Skills

- ☐ Incomplete mastery of basic facts (e.g., mathematical tables)
- ☐ Reverses numbers (e.g., 123 or 321 or 231)
- ☐ Confuses operational symbols, especially + and ×
- ☐ Copies problems incorrectly from one line to another
- ☐ Difficulty comprehending word problems
- ☐ Difficulty understanding key concepts and applications to aid problem solving

❺ Organizational and Study Skills

- ☐ Difficulty with organization skills
- ☐ Time management difficulties
- ☐ Slow to start and complete tasks
- ☐ Repeated inability, on a day-to-day basis, to recall what has been taught
- ☐ Lack of overall organization in taking notes
- ☐ Difficulty interpreting charts and graphs
- ☐ Inefficient use of library and reference materials
- ☐ Difficulty preparing for and taking tests.

❻ Attention and Concentration

- ☐ Trouble focusing and sustaining attention on academic tasks
- ☐ Fluctuating attention span during lectures
- ☐ Easily distractible by outside stimuli
- ☐ Difficulty juggling multiple task demands and overloads quickly
- ☐ Hyperactivity and excessive movements may accompany the inability to focus attention
- ☐ Trouble meeting people or working cooperatively with others

Source: Unlocking Potential: College and Other Choices for People with LD and ADHD (pp. 264–265), by J. M. Taymans, L. L. West, and M. Sullivan (Eds.), 2000, Bethesda, MD: Woodbine House. Copyright 2000 by J. M. Taymans, L. L. West, and M. Sullivan. Adapted with permission.

Name _____   Date _____

Your Learning Style

☼ Put a ✓ beside all of the statements that apply to your learning style.

Visual

_____ **1.** I remember something better if I write it down.

_____ **2.** I like to doodle while I am taking notes.

_____ **3.** It helps me to look at a person when trying to listen.

_____ **4.** I am good at reading maps and charts.

_____ **5.** I remember what I see better than what I hear.

_____ **6.** I can recall people's faces more easily than I can recall their names.

_____ **7.** My written work doesn't look neat to me.

_____ **8.** My eyes get tired fast, even though the eye doctor says they are okay.

_____ **9.** It helps me to use my fingers as a pointer when reading.

_____ **10.** If I am taking a test, I can "see" the textbook page where the answer is.

_____ **Total number of check marks**

Auditory

_____ **1.** I can remember the words to a song after hearing it a few times.

_____ **2.** I would rather listen to the teacher than read a textbook.

_____ **3.** I understand how to do something if someone "tells" me.

_____ **4.** I often talk to myself when I am thinking.

_____ **5.** I like to participate in classroom discussions.

_____ **6.** I remember things more easily if I repeat them out loud.

_____ **7.** I can concentrate on something despite a lot of noise around me.

_____ **8.** It's hard for me to understand a joke someone tells me.

_____ **9.** I like to work in quiet places.

_____ **10.** It's hard for me to understand what someone is saying if other people are talking around me.

_____ **Total number of check marks**

➜

Source: Original source unknown. See Author Note on p. 8.

Kinesthetic/Tactile/Hands-on

_____ **1.** I am very good at sports.

_____ **2.** I would rather work on a project than just read about it.

_____ **3.** Studying at a desk is not for me.

_____ **4.** I don't like to read directions. I'd rather just start doing.

_____ **5.** I do not become easily lost, even in strange surroundings.

_____ **6.** I think better if I am able to move around.

_____ **7.** I work well with my hands doing things such as puzzles or using tools.

_____ **8.** I tend to use my fingers when I am counting in my head.

_____ **9.** I need a lot of breaks when I am studying.

_____ **10.** Before I follow directions, it helps me to see someone else do it first.

_____ **Total number of check marks**

Source: Original source unknown. See Author Note on p. 8.

Name _____   Date _____

C.I.T.E. Learning Styles

☼ **Circle the number that most closely matches your learning style.**

		Most Like Me			Least Like Me
1.	When I make things for my studies, I remember what I have learned better.........	4	3	2	1
2.	Written assignments are easy for me to do....................................	4	3	2	1
3.	I learn better if someone reads a book to me than if I read silently to myself.........	4	3	2	1
4.	I learn best when I study alone.	4	3	2	1
5.	Having assignment directions written on the board makes them easier to understand.	4	3	2	1
6.	It's harder for me to do a written assignment than an oral one.	4	3	2	1
7.	When I do math problems, I say the numbers to myself....................	4	3	2	1
8.	If I need help in the subject, I will ask a classmate for help.....................	4	3	2	1
9.	I understand a math problem that is written down better than one I hear.	4	3	2	1
10.	I don't mind doing written assignments.	4	3	2	1
11.	I remember things I hear better than I read.	4	3	2	1
12.	I remember more of what I learn if I learn it when I am alone....................	4	3	2	1
13.	I would rather read a story than listen to it being read.	4	3	2	1
14.	I feel like I talk smarter than I write....................................	4	3	2	1
15.	If someone tells me three numbers to add, I can usually get the right answer without writing them down.	4	3	2	1
16.	I like to work in a group because I learn from the others in my group..............	4	3	2	1
17.	Written math problems are easier for me to do than oral ones.	4	3	2	1
18.	Writing a spelling word several times helps me remember it better.	4	3	2	1
19.	I find it easier to remember what I have heard than what I have read.............	4	3	2	1
20.	It is more fun to learn with classmates at first, but it is hard to study with them.	4	3	2	1
21.	I like written directions better than spoken ones.	4	3	2	1
22.	If homework were oral, I would do it all..................................	4	3	2	1
23.	When I hear a phone number I can remember it without writing it down..........	4	3	2	1
24.	I get more done when I work with someone.	4	3	2	1
25.	Seeing a number makes more sense to me than hearing a number.	4	3	2	1
26.	I like to do things like simple repairs or crafts with my hands...................	4	3	2	1
27.	The things I write on paper sound better than when I say them..................	4	3	2	1
28.	I study best when no one is around to talk or listen to.	4	3	2	1
29.	I would rather read things in a book than have the teacher tell me about them.	4	3	2	1

➡

Source: C.I.T.E. Learning Styles Instrument, by A. M. Babich, P. Burdine, L. Allbright, and P. Randol, Wichita, KS: Wichita Public Schools. Adapted with permission.

	Most Like Me			Least Like Me

30. Speaking is a better way than writing if you want someone to understand what you really mean. **4 3 2 1**

31. When I have a written math problem to do, I say it to myself to understand it better. **4 3 2 1**

32. I can learn more about a subject if I am with a small group of students. **4 3 2 1**

33. Seeing the price of something written down is easier for me to understand than having someone tell me the price. **4 3 2 1**

34. I like to make things with my hands. **4 3 2 1**

35. I like tests that call for sentence completion or written answers. **4 3 2 1**

36. I understand more from a class discussion than from reading about a subject. **4 3 2 1**

37. I remember the spelling of a word better if I see it written down than if someone spells it out loud. **4 3 2 1**

38. Spelling and grammar rules make it hard for me to say what I want to in writing. **4 3 2 1**

39. It makes it easier when I say the numbers of a problem to myself as I work it out. **4 3 2 1**

40. I like to study with other people. **4 3 2 1**

41. When teachers say a number I really don't understand it until I see it written down. **4 3 2 1**

42. I understand what I have learned better when I am involved in making something for the subject. **4 3 2 1**

43. Sometimes I say dumb things, but writing gives me time to correct myself. **4 3 2 1**

44. I do well on tests if they are about things I hear in class. **4 3 2 1**

45. I can't think as well when I work with someone else. **4 3 2 1**

Source: C.I.T.E. Learning Styles Instrument, by A. M. Babich, P. Burdine, L. Allbright, and P. Randol, Wichita, KS: Wichita Public Schools. Adapted with permission.

Write the number you circled for each of the items on the previous two pages in the categories below. Total each list, then multiply by 2 for the category score. Review the total scores to find the category with the highest number. Refer to the category descriptions on p. 85 to learn more about your learning style.

Auditory Language

3 ____

11 ____

19 ____   Total ____ × 2 = ____ (score)

36 ____

44 ____

Visual Language

5 ____

13 ____

21 ____   Total ____ × 2 = ____ (score)

29 ____

37 ____

Auditory Numerical

7 ____

15 ____

23 ____   Total ____ × 2 = ____ (score)

31 ____

39 ____

Visual Numerical

9 ____

17 ____

25 ____   Total ____ × 2 = ____ (score)

33 ____

41 ____

Auditory-Kinesthetic-Tactile

1 ____

18 ____

26 ____   Total ____ × 2 = ____ (score)

34 ____

42 ____

Individual Learner

4 ____

12 ____

20 ____   Total ____ × 2 = ____ (score)

28 ____

45 ____

Group Learner

8 ____

16 ____

24 ____   Total ____ × 2 = ____ (score)

32 ____

40 ____

Oral Expressive

6 ____

14 ____

22 ____   Total ____ × 2 = ____ (score)

30 ____

38 ____

Written Expressive

2 ____

10 ____

27 ____   Total ____ × 2 = ____ (score)

35 ____

43 ____

Source: C.I.T.E. Learning Styles Instrument, by A. M. Babich, P. Burdine, L. Allbright, and P. Randol, Wichita, KS: Wichita Public Schools. Adapted with permission.

Auditory Language

Learns from hearing words spoken. He or she may vocalize or move his or her lips or throat while reading, particularly when striving to understand new material. He or she will be more capable of understanding and remembering words or facts that have been learned by hearing.

Visual Language

Learns well from seeing words in books, on the chalkboard, charts, or workbooks. He or she may even write down words that are given orally, in order to learn by seeing them on paper. This person remembers and uses information better if he or she has read it.

Auditory Numerical

Learns from hearing numbers and oral explanations. Remembering telephone and locker numbers is easy, and he or she may be successful with oral number games and puzzles. This person may do just as well without a math book, for written materials are not important. He or she can probably work problems in his/her head, and may say numbers out loud when reading.

Visual Numerical

Must see numbers—the board, in a book, or on a paper—in order to work with them. He or she is more likely to remember and understand math facts when they are presented visually but doesn't seem to need as much oral explanation.

Auditory-Visual-Kinesthetic Combination

Learns best by doing, becoming involved with the material. He or she profits from a combination of stimuli. The manipulation of material along with accompanying sight and sounds (words and numbers seen and heard) will aid his or her learning. They may not seem to understand or be able to concentrate on work unless totally involved. He or she seeks to handle, touch, and work with what he or she is learning.

Individual Learner

Gets more work done alone. He or she thinks best and remembers more when the learning has been done alone.

Group Learner

Prefers to study with at least one other person and will not get as much done alone. He or she values others' opinions and preferences. Group interaction increases his or her learning and later recognition of facts.

Oral Expressive

Prefers to tell what he or she knows. He or she talks fluently, comfortably, and clearly. This person may know more than written tests show. He or she is probably less shy than others about giving reports or talking. Muscular coordination involved in writing may be difficult for this person. Organizing and putting thoughts on paper may be too slow and tedious a task for this student.

Written Expressive

Prefers to write fluent essays and good answers on tests to show what he or she knows. He or she feels less comfortable when oral answers or reports are required. His or her thoughts are better organized on paper than when they are given orally.

Source: C.I.T.E. Learning Styles Instrument, by A. M. Babich, P. Burdine, L. Allbright, and P. Randol, Wichita, KS: Wichita Public Schools. Adapted with permission.

Name _____ Date _____

Learning-Related Preferences

☀ **Place a check mark beside all preferences that are most true for you in each situation.**

1. When I read or work on *assignments* at **school**, I prefer

   _____ Total quiet

   _____ Normal background noise

   _____ A space separated from view of other people

   _____ A space where I can get up and walk around

   _____ A small, cozy space

   _____ A well-lighted room

   _____ A room with dim lights with a reading light

2. When I read or work on *assignments* at **home**, I prefer

   _____ Total quiet

   _____ Normal background noise

   _____ My choice of music playing

   _____ A space separated from view of other people

   _____ A space where I can get up and walk around

   _____ A small, cozy space

   _____ A well-lighted room

   _____ A room with dim lights with a reading light

3. When I study for *exams* at **school**, I prefer

   _____ Total quiet

   _____ Normal background noise

   _____ A space separated from view of other people

   _____ A space where I can get up and walk around

   _____ A small, cozy space

   _____ A well-lighted room

   _____ A room with dim lights with a reading light

4. When I study for *exams* at **home**, I prefer

   _____ Total quiet

   _____ Normal background noise

   _____ My choice of music playing

   _____ A space separated from view of other people

   _____ A space where I can get up and walk around

   _____ A small, cozy space

   _____ A well-lighted room

   _____ A room with dim lights with a reading light

5. When I am *listening* to get information at **school**, I prefer

   _____ To be close enough to hear everything

   _____ In a well-lighted room

   _____ Using a hearing-assistance device

6. When I am *looking at materials* to get information, I prefer:

   _____ Have good light on the material

   _____ Be close enough to see everything

   _____ Be in a darkened room with learning materials under bright light

7. When I can choose the time of day to read, study, or do homework, I prefer:

   _____ Early to mid-morning

   _____ Before exercise

   _____ Mid-morning to noon

   _____ After exercise

   _____ Early afternoon to mid-afternoon

   _____ Before eating a meal

   _____ Mid-afternoon to early evening

   _____ After eating a meal

   _____ Early evening to 10:00 PM

   _____ A time when I can have snacks and soda or coffee

   _____ After 10:00 PM

Name _____   Date _____

At-College Checklist

☀ **Put a check mark in the box beside each step you have completed.**

☐ I have met with the disability resource office staff to discuss my courses and whether I will need accommodations.

☐ I am taking the advice of the disability resource office staff, and I am following through with their recommendations.

☐ Where recommended, I have asked the learning disability resource office to write letters to my professors describing my learning disability and requesting specific accommodations.

☐ I have talked to my professors about my learning disability and the accommodations I need for their courses.

☐ I have developed a strong network of friends with whom I can share my joys and frustrations.

☐ I am using a daily/weekly/monthly planner to keep well organized.

☐ I have a place to study that is suitable to my learning style, and I am using this location on a consistent basis.

☐ I have learned how to use my college library.

☐ I have located a free tutoring service on campus. *(If available)*

☐ I have arranged for a private tutoring service on campus. *(If necessary)*

☐ I am studying on average 2 to 4 hours daily.

☐ I am watching my progress closely. If I become overwhelmed by my course load, I am prepared to take fewer courses.

☐ During each college year, I am trying to reduce my need for accommodations.

Source: Transitions To Postsecondary Learning: Self-Advocacy Handbook for Students with Learning Disabilities and/or Attention Deficit Disorder (p. 65), by H. Eaton and L. Coull, 1998, Vancouver, BC, Canada: Eaton Coull Learning Group. Copyright 1998 by Eaton Coull Learning Group. Adapted with permission.

Student Name _____ Date _____

Completed by _____

Functional-Needs Interview

1. Which of the following areas do we need to work on to help you meet your goals? Please tell me all that apply to you.

____ Reading

____ Seeing things around the room

____ Writing/Spelling

____ Doing math

____ Paying attention

____ Staying on track

____ Getting used to changes in the classroom

____ Remembering

____ Getting frustrated

____ Hearing the teacher

____ Talking with the teacher and others

____ Getting my ideas across to the teachers and others

____ Getting into or around in the classroom

____ Sitting still or in one place for very long

★ *Refer to the in-depth interview on the following pages for each checked issue above.*

2. Are there any other areas in which you think you need help?

_____

_____

Let's put all of these areas in order of importance, most important being first.

_____

3. Did you have problems in these areas when you were in school?

_____

4. Do you have any records from school or any other agency (like an IEP or test information) or any other information from a teacher or a counselor?

_____

_____

5. Are you taking any medications that might affect your school work? Medications that make you drowsy, thirsty, or nauseated?

_____

_____

Source: Accommodations: Accommodating Adults with Disabilities in Adult Education Programs (pp. 1–11), by University of Kansas Institute for Adult Studies, 1998, Lawrence: Author. Copyright 1998 by University of Kansas Center for Research on Learning. Adapted with permission.

❶ Is reading hard because it is difficult to see things on the page? _____
   (If no, skip the rest of this section, and go to section 2 on the next page.)

   ◼ Has a doctor told you that you have an eye problem that is causing problems with your vision? _____

   ◼ Can you name or describe the problem? _____

   ◼ Is your vision changing now? _____

   ◼ Is your vision expected to stay the same? _____

   ◼ Which of the following are true? Tell me all that apply to you.

      ____ Having the lighting just right is important for me.

      ____ Regular-size print is hard for me to read.

      ____ Using very dark print is important for me.

      ____ I read slowly.

      ____ I have trouble making sense of what I read.

      ____ I have trouble following the print all the way across the page.

      ____ I skip lines when I'm reading.

      ____ Other (specify) _____

   ◼ Do you have a problem reading your mail? If yes, how do you solve this problem?

   _____

   _____

   ◼ Do you have a problem reading labels, prices, or expiration dates in the grocery store? If yes, how do you solve this problem?

   _____

   _____

   ◼ Do you have any ideas of what might help you do better in these areas? Maybe something that has worked for you in the past? If so, what is it?

   _____

   _____

   ◼ Were there things that you tried to improve your reading that didn't work or didn't work well? If yes, what were these things?

   _____

   _____

   ◼ Is there anything else about your reading that you would like us to know?

   _____

   _____

Source: Accommodations: Accommodating Adults with Disabilities in Adult Education Programs (pp. 1–11), by University of Kansas Institute for Adult Studies, 1998, Lawrence: Author. Copyright 1998 by University of Kansas Center for Research on Learning. Adapted with permission.

❷ Do you feel that your eyes are okay but you have trouble reading for some other reason? If yes, what is the reason?

◾ Which of the following is true? Tell me all that apply to you.

___ I have trouble concentrating when I read.

___ I have trouble remembering what I have read.

___ I have trouble figuring out words.

___ I can read the words, but I don't understand them.

___ I read too slowly.

___ Other_____

◾ Do you have a problem reading your mail? If yes, how do you solve this problem?

_____

_____

◾ Do you have a problem reading the menu at a restaurant? If yes, how do you solve this problem?

_____

_____

◾ Do you have any ideas of what might help you do better in these areas? Maybe something that has worked for you in the past? If so, what is it?

_____

_____

◾ Were there things that you tried to improve your reading that didn't work or didn't work well? If yes, what were these things?

_____

_____

◾ Is there anything else about your reading that you would like us to know?

_____

_____

Source: Accommodations: Accommodating Adults with Disabilities in Adult Education Programs (pp. 1–11), by University of Kansas Institute for Adult Studies, 1998, Lawrence: Author. Copyright 1998 by University of Kansas Center for Research on Learning. Adapted with permission.

- ◼ Which of the following are true? Tell me all that apply to you.

    ____ Regular-size pencils are hard for me to hold.

    ____ Staying on the lines of paper is hard for me.

    ____ Writing on paper that doesn't have lines is very hard.

    ____ I have trouble holding the paper down or keeping it still.

    ____ I write very slowly.

    ____ Sometimes I forget what I'm supposed to be writing down.

    ____ I forget which way some of the letters and numbers are supposed to go.

    ____ I can't remember how to spell words.

    ____ I have a hard time putting my thoughts down on paper so that it makes sense to someone else.

- ◼ Do you have a problem signing your name? If yes, what do you do?

    _____

    _____

- ◼ Do you have a problem filling out forms (such as when applying for a job, paying taxes, etc.)? If yes, how do you solve this problem?

    _____

    _____

- ◼ Do you have a problem when leaving a note for someone? If yes, how do you solve this problem?

    _____

    _____

- ◼ Do you have any ideas of what might help you do better in these areas? Maybe something that has worked for you in the past? If so, what is it?

    _____

    _____

- ◼ Were there things that you tried to improve your writing that didn't work or didn't work well? If yes, what were these things?

    _____

    _____

- ◼ Is there anything else about your writing that you would like us to know?

    _____

    _____

Source: *Accommodations: Accommodating Adults with Disabilities in Adult Education Programs* (pp. 1–11), by University of Kansas Institute for Adult Studies, 1998, Lawrence: Author. Copyright 1998 by University of Kansas Center for Research on Learning. Adapted with permission.

◾ Which of the following statements is true? Tell me all that apply to you.

    ___ I write or copy numbers down wrong (out of order or backwards).

    ___ Word problems don't make sense to me.

    ___ I get confused by symbols like + and −.

    ___ I feel like I know what to do to solve a problem, but I don't know how to go about it.

    ___ I have a problem keeping numbers in the right columns when adding.

◾ Do you have a problem counting money or knowing whether you got the correct change? If yes, how do you solve this problem?

_____

_____

◾ Do you have any ideas of what might help you do better in these areas? Maybe something that has worked for you in the past? If so, what is it?

_____

_____

◾ Were there things that you tried to improve your math that didn't work or didn't work well? If yes, what were these things?

_____

_____

◾ Is there any other information about your math that you would like us to know?

_____

_____

Source: Accommodations: Accommodating Adults with Disabilities in Adult Education Programs (pp. 1–11), by University of Kansas Institute for Adult Studies, 1998, Lawrence: Author. Copyright 1998 by University of Kansas Center for Research on Learning. Adapted with permission.

◼ Which of the following are true? Check all that apply.

    ____ I have a hard time remembering directions that the teacher has just given me.

    ____ I have a hard time remembering what I just read.

    ____ I have a hard time remembering how to use what I just learned when I am supposed to apply it (like working on a math problem or writing a paragraph).

    ____ I have a hard time keeping my place when I read or write.

    ____ I always seem to have trouble figuring out where to put things on the desk/table so that I can do the work I am supposed to do.

◼ It is hard for me to follow along from one task to the next, like finishing one math problem and moving on to the next.

◼ It takes me longer than everybody else to switch from one subject to another, like from reading to math or from writing to social studies.

◼ I have a hard time concentrating when new people come into the room.

◼ I have a hard time concentrating when we change the day's schedule and things are different from how I expected them to be.

◼ I start to daydream, even when I am trying very hard to pay attention.

◼ Do you have a problem keeping things straight when somebody gives you directions to get somewhere? If yes, how do you solve this problem?

◼ Do you have a problem making sure that you don't lose your keys? If yes, how do you solve this problem?

◼ Do you have a problem keeping track of your bills and important papers at home? If yes, how do you solve this problem?

◼ Do you have any ideas of what might help you do better in these areas? Maybe something that has worked for you in the past? If so, what is it?

◼ Were there things that you tried to improve your organization that didn't work or didn't work well? If yes, what were these things?

◼ Is there anything else about how you organize that you would like us to know?

Source: Accommodations: Accommodating Adults with Disabilities in Adult Education Programs (pp. 1–11), by University of Kansas Institute for Adult Studies, 1998, Lawrence: Author. Copyright 1998 by University of Kansas Center for Research on Learning. Adapted with permission.

◼ Which of the following statements are true? Tell me all that apply to you.

____ I get angry with my teachers when they can't help me figure something out.

____ I get angry with my teachers when they expect me to know more than I do.

____ I get angry with other learners when they make too much noise or get in my way when I am trying to pay attention.

____ I get frustrated when I can't learn something, and I take it out on the teacher or other learners.

____ I get angry with myself and give up.

◼ What do you do when you feel yourself beginning to get frustrated?

_____

_____

◼ Do you have any ideas of what might help you do better in these areas? Maybe something that has worked for you in the past? If so, what is it?

_____

_____

◼ Were there things that you tried when you felt yourself getting frustrated that didn't work or didn't work well? If yes, what were these things?

_____

_____

◼ Is there anything else about getting frustrated that you would like us to know?

_____

_____

◼ Has a doctor told you that you have a problem that keeps you from hearing as well as you should?

_____

_____

◼ Has your hearing stayed the same for some time, and is it expected to stay the same?

_____

_____

◼ Which of the following statements are true? Tell me all that apply to you.

____ I can't hear the teacher all the time.

____ I can hear the teacher only if he or she sits or stands right in front of me or to one side.

____ I can't hear the teacher when there is noise in the room.

____ I can read lips.

____ I use sign language. If yes, what kind? (e.g., ASL, SEE, etc.)

____ I use a TDD, telecommunications device, or special telephone for the deaf.

◼ Do you have a problem getting information from someone in the bank or at the Social Security office or at your child's school, etc? If so, what do you do to get the information you need?

_____

_____

◼ Do you have a problem following what is going on at meetings or at the movies? If yes, how do you solve this problem?

_____

_____

◼ Do you have any ideas of what might help you do better in these areas? Maybe something that has worked for you in the past? If so, what is it?

_____

_____

◼ Were there things that you tried to improve your hearing that didn't work or didn't work well? If yes, what were these things?

_____

_____

◼ Is there anything else about your hearing that you would like us to know?

_____

_____

Source: Accommodations: Accommodating Adults with Disabilities in Adult Education Programs (pp. 1–11), by University of Kansas Institute for Adult Studies, 1998, Lawrence: Author. Copyright 1998 by University of Kansas Center for Research on Learning. Adapted with permission.

◼ Which of the following are true? Tell me all that apply to you.

____ Other people often have a problem understanding what I say.

____ I don't speak English very well, and others can't understand me.

____ I have a hard time figuring out what I want to say to the teacher. It doesn't come out right.

____ I have a hard time asking for what I need.

____ Since I can't hear, communication back and forth with people who speak is hard for me.

◼ Do you have a problem giving someone directions when they ask you for them? If so, what do you do when this happens?

_____

_____

◼ Is it hard for people to understand you on the phone? If yes, what do you do?

_____

_____

◼ Do you have any ideas of what might help you do better in these areas? Maybe something that has worked for you in the past? If so, what is it?

_____

_____

◼ Were there things that you tried to improve your speech that didn't work or didn't work well? If yes, what were these things?

_____

_____

◼ Is there anything else about your speech that you would like us to know?

_____

_____

Source: Accommodations: Accommodating Adults with Disabilities in Adult Education Programs (pp. 1–11), by University of Kansas Institute for Adult Studies, 1998, Lawrence: Author. Copyright 1998 by University of Kansas Center for Research on Learning. Adapted with permission.

■ Do you have any of the following problems when getting into the classroom? Tell me if any of these apply to you.

___ I can't get myself to the classroom in my wheelchair.

___ I can't get my wheelchair through the door of the classroom.

___ I can't move my wheelchair around the room once inside.

___ I can't walk all the way to the room.

___ I can't see things in the way when I am walking.

■ Do you have any ideas of what might help you do better in these areas? Maybe something that has worked for you in the past? If so, what is it?

_____

_____

■ Were there things that you tried to improve your ability to get into a classroom or move around in a classroom that didn't work or didn't work well? If yes, what were these things?

_____

_____

■ Is there anything else about getting around that you would like us to know?

_____

_____

Source: Accommodations: Accommodating Adults with Disabilities in Adult Education Programs (pp. 1–11), by University of Kansas Institute for Adult Studies, 1998, Lawrence: Author. Copyright 1998 by University of Kansas Center for Research on Learning. Adapted with permission.

◼ I have trouble sitting for long periods because _____. Tell me all that apply to you.

___ I get very tired

___ It hurts me or is uncomfortable for me.

___ I get "antsy." I need to move around.

___ I need to change position to keep a sore from starting or getting worse.

___ I need to take a break to clear my head.

◼ I can stay still for _____ minutes/hours when I am doing school work. After that I need to get up because

_____

_____

◼ Is there anything that you do or know about that might help you in this area? If so, what is it?

_____

_____

◼ Were there things that you tried to help you sit for long periods that didn't work or worked only a little? What were these things?

_____

_____

◼ Is there anything else about sitting in one place that you would like us to know?

_____

_____

Source: Accommodations: Accommodating Adults with Disabilities in Adult Education Programs (pp. 1–11), by University of Kansas Institute for Adult Studies, 1998, Lawrence: Author. Copyright 1998 by University of Kansas Center for Research on Learning. Adapted with permission.

Name _____   Date _____

Accommodations for Academic Support

| | Is this a problem for me? | | | |
Activity	Yes	Somewhat	No	Possible Solutions

Participating in Class

Activity	Yes	Somewhat	No	Possible Solutions
1. Getting out materials for note-taking	☐	☐	☐	_____
2. Taking notes	☐	☐	☐	_____
3. Asking and answering questions (communication)	☐	☐	☐	_____
4. Working on group projects, if required	☐	☐	☐	_____
5. Hearing the instructor	☐	☐	☐	_____
6. Hearing and contributing to large-group discussions	☐	☐	☐	_____
7. Hearing and contributing to small-group discussions	☐	☐	☐	_____
8. Participating in group presentations	☐	☐	☐	_____
9. Hearing and seeing classroom demonstrations	☐	☐	☐	_____
10. Participating in laboratory or studio sessions and groups	☐	☐	☐	_____
11. Completing papers and written assignments	☐	☐	☐	_____

Accessing Class Information

Activity	Yes	Somewhat	No	Possible Solutions
1. Overheads (prepared and real-time)	☐	☐	☐	_____
2. Handouts	☐	☐	☐	_____
3. Readings	☐	☐	☐	_____
3. E-readings	☐	☐	☐	_____
4. Textbooks	☐	☐	☐	_____
5. E-textbooks	☐	☐	☐	_____
6. E-mail	☐	☐	☐	_____
7. Document cameras	☐	☐	☐	_____
8. PA systems	☐	☐	☐	_____
10. Demonstration equipment and props	☐	☐	☐	_____
11. Whiteboard/Blackboard	☐	☐	☐	_____
12. Slides	☐	☐	☐	_____
13. Filmstrips	☐	☐	☐	_____

Source: I.A.A.M.: Student Activity Checklist (pp. 9–11), by R. O. Smith, J. Warnke, D. Edyburn, D. Mellard, N. Kurth, and G. Berry, 2002, Lawrence: University of Kansas Center for Research on Learning Division of Adult Studies. Copyright 2002 by University of Kansas Center for Research on Learning. Adapted with permission.

Activity	Is this a problem for me?			Possible Solutions
	Yes	Somewhat	No	
14. Films	☐	☐	☐	_____
15. Videos	☐	☐	☐	_____
16. Television	☐	☐	☐	_____
17. Closed Circuit Television (CCTV)	☐	☐	☐	_____
18 Web sites and Web presentations	☐	☐	☐	_____
19. Educational computer software	☐	☐	☐	_____
20. Computer presentations (PowerPoint)	☐	☐	☐	_____

Testing and Evaluation

Activity	Yes	Somewhat	No	Possible Solutions
1. Taking tests in class	☐	☐	☐	_____
2. Taking standardized (district/state) tests	☐	☐	☐	_____
3. Taking national tests	☐	☐	☐	_____
4. Taking placement tests	☐	☐	☐	_____
5. Taking lab tests and quizzes	☐	☐	☐	_____
6. Taking oral examinations	☐	☐	☐	_____
7. Taking multiple choice tests (including those with computer graded bubble forms)	☐	☐	☐	_____
8. Taking essay tests	☐	☐	☐	_____
9. Taking pop quizzes	☐	☐	☐	_____

Others

Activity	Yes	Somewhat	No	Possible Solutions
1. _____	☐	☐	☐	_____
2. _____	☐	☐	☐	_____
3. _____	☐	☐	☐	_____
4. _____	☐	☐	☐	_____

Source: I.A.A.M.: Student Activity Checklist (pp. 9–11), by R. O. Smith, J. Warnke, D. Edyburn, D. Mellard, N. Kurth, and G. Berry, 2002, Lawrence: University of Kansas Center for Research on Learning Division of Adult Studies. Copyright 2002 by University of Kansas Center for Research on Learning. Adapted with permission.

Information About College Courses

Course	Faculty	Offered Term, Time	Reading Amount, Level	% of Time		Assessments			
				Lecture	Hands-on	Performance	Exams	Papers	Attendance

Source: Preparing for Postsecondary Education and Training: Overview Information Strategies (p. 2), by K. B. Flannery, R. Slovic, M. C. Dalmald, S. Bigaj, and N. Hart, 2000, Eugene: University of Oregon. Copyright 2000 by University of Oregon. Adapted with permission.

Name _____   Date _____

Course _____   Instructor _____

Course-Analysis Guide

Course Materials

1. Which of these materials are used in this course?

	Degree of Usage				
	Never	◄·····················►			Constant
___ Required texts	1	2	3	4	5
___ Optional texts	1	2	3	4	5
___ Reserve readings	1	2	3	4	5
___ Handouts	1	2	3	4	5
___ Internet resources	1	2	3	4	5
___ Other _____	1	2	3	4	5

Content Presentation

1. Which format is used in class sessions?

	Relative Frequency				
	Never	◄·····················►			Always
___ Lecture	1	2	3	4	5
___ Class discussion	1	2	3	4	5
___ Small-group activities	1	2	3	4	5
___ Specific in-class assignments (e.g., writing assignments)	1	2	3	4	5
___ Student presentation/performance	1	2	3	4	5
___ Other _____	1	2	3	4	5

2. Which instructional techniques are used in the course?

	Degree of Usage				
	Never	◄·····················►			Constant
___ Handouts	1	2	3	4	5
___ Advance organizers (lecture outlines)	1	2	3	4	5
___ Computer-based presentations	1	2	3	4	5
___ Overhead projector	1	2	3	4	5
___ Other audiovisual aids _____	1	2	3	4	5
___ Blackboard	1	2	3	4	5
___ Internet-based activities	1	2	3	4	5
___ Field-based experience	1	2	3	4	5
___ Other _____	1	2	3	4	5

3. Are there personal idiosyncrasies of the instructor(s) that may positively or negatively affect student's success in the course?

_____

Source: "Analyzing College Courses," by J. R. Patton and E. A. Polloway, 1987, *Academic Therapy, 22,* pp. 273–280. Austin, TX: PRO-ED. Copyright 1987 by PRO-ED, Inc. Adapted with permission.

Student Responsibilities

1. Which tasks are students required to do in class?

	Relative Frequency			
Never	◄┄┄┄┄┄┄►			Always

___ Note-taking from lectures and presentations   1   2   3   4   5

___ Respond to direct questioning   1   2   3   4   5

___ Reading assignments   1   2   3   4   5

___ Writing assignments   1   2   3   4   5

___ Independent work activities   1   2   3   4   5

___ Small-group work/discussion   1   2   3   4   5

___ Class participation   1   2   3   4   5

___ Class oral presentation   1   2   3   4   5

___ Other _____   1   2   3   4   5

2. Which tasks are students required to do out of class?

	Relative Frequency			
Never	◄┄┄┄┄┄┄►			Always

___ Reading assignments   1   2   3   4   5

___ Writing assignments   1   2   3   4   5

___ Internet-based activities   1   2   3   4   5

___ Short papers   1   2   3   4   5

___ Term papers   1   2   3   4   5

___ Field work   1   2   3   4   5

___ Course projects   1   2   3   4   5

___ Interviews   1   2   3   4   5

___ Extra credit (options available)   1   2   3   4   5

___ Other _____   1   2   3   4   5

Student Evaluation

1. How are students evaluated in this course?

	Degree of Usage			
Never	◄┄┄┄┄┄┄►			Constant

___ Tests   1   2   3   4   5

___ Papers   1   2   3   4   5

___ Performance measures   1   2   3   4   5

___ In-class presentations   1   2   3   4   5

___ Projects (group)   1   2   3   4   5

___ Projects (individual)   1   2   3   4   5

___ Field work   1   2   3   4   5

___ Other _____   1   2   3   4   5

Source: "Analyzing College Courses," by J. R. Patton and E. A. Polloway, 1987, *Academic Therapy, 22,* pp. 273–280. Austin, TX: PRO-ED. Copyright 1987 by PRO-ED, Inc. Adapted with permission.

2. What types of tests and test items are used in this course?

	Degree of Usage				
	Never	◀·················▶			Always
No testing is done	1	2	3	4	5
Essay	1	2	3	4	5
Multiple choice	1	2	3	4	5
Other objective tests (i.e., matching, T/F)	1	2	3	4	5
Completion/short answer	1	2	3	4	5
Oral exams	1	2	3	4	5
Performance of skill	1	2	3	4	5
Other _____	1	2	3	4	5

Classroom Standards

1. What standards apply in this class? Are they stated or implied? (*Please specify*)

____ Attendance _____

____ Lateness _____

____ Attentiveness during class _____

____ Preparation _____

    ____ Coursework (e.g., reading assignments) _____

    ____ Materials for class _____

____ Grade of incomplete _____

____ Other _____

2 How is feedback given to students?

____ Grades only

____ Corrective feedback (i.e., comments)

____ Primary focus on errors

____ Other _____

3. Are there other special requirements that contribute to student evaluation (e.g., typing of papers, late acceptance)?

_____

_____

_____

4. Are there stipulations that interfere with the use of tape recorders (Y/N), interpreters (Y/N), note takers (Y/N)?

_____

_____

_____

Source: "Analyzing College Courses," by J. R. Patton and E. A. Polloway, 1987, *Academic Therapy, 22,* pp. 273–280. Austin, TX: PRO-ED. Copyright 1987 by PRO-ED, Inc. Adapted with permission.

Student Supports

		Degree of Availability				
		Never ◄·····················► **Always**				

1. Which of the following course-related support systems are available?

	Never				Always
___ Accommodation of student needs	1	2	3	4	5
___ Instructor access	1	2	3	4	5
___ Teaching assistant(s) access	1	2	3	4	5
___ Course mailing list (i.e., Listserve)	1	2	3	4	5
___ Web-based resources	1	2	3	4	5
___ Special study sessions	1	2	3	4	5
___ Peer-support mechanisms	1	2	3	4	5
___ Other _____	1	2	3	4	5

Source: "Analyzing College Courses," by J. R. Patton and E. A. Polloway, 1987, *Academic Therapy, 22,* pp. 273–280. Austin, TX: PRO-ED. Copyright 1987 by PRO-ED, Inc. Adapted with permission.

Helpful Study Strategies

☀ **Put a check mark beside the strategies that you are already using.**

Note-Taking

❑ I take notes from lectures.

❑ I get the important points from my teachers' lectures.

❑ I use different ways to take accurate notes.

❑ I use abbreviations for note-taking.

❑ I turn my notes into study sheets.

❑ I combine information from the textbook with my lecture notes.

❑ I review my notes over a period of time.

Memorization

❑ I know different ways to memorize besides reading information over and over.

❑ I use different ways to memorize information.

❑ When I take tests, I remember most of the facts I tried to memorize.

Test-Taking

❑ While taking a test, I very carefully follow directions.

❑ I use appropriate strategies for taking different kinds of tests.

❑ I keep old tests to use at a later time.

❑ I analyze my errors from old tests to determine a pattern.

❑ I effectively prepare for mid-terms and final exams.

❑ I know strategies to help me reduce stress and relax.

Doing Homework

❑ I use an assignment book.

❑ I spend enough time on homework to do a thorough job.

❑ I complete homework by the time it is due.

Source: Study Strategies Made Easy (p. 2), by L. Davis and S. Sirotowitz, 1996, Plantation, FL: Specialty Press. Copyright 1996 by L. Davis and S. Sirotowitz. Adapted with permission.

Name _____   Date _____

Assistive Technology Communication Needs

☼ **Describe specific needs in the settings listed below.**

	At Work	At School	At Home	In the Community
Reading Computer • text and screen reading programs • scan-and-speak programs • text enhancement software Electronic books Page turners				
Writing Computer • word processing • spell checker and writing support (e.g., grammar check) • speech recognition programs • outlining • brain storming Alternative keyboard Adapted grips (pen) Adapted paper Slant board				
Speaking/Expressive Language Augmentative and alternative systems Augmentative and alternative devices (e.g., picture communication boards, electronic boards/speech production)				
Listening Assistive listening device (e.g., FM) Voice recording devices Speech-to-print programs				

Source: Assistive Technology Communication Needs (p. 144), by G. M. Clark, J. R. Patton, and L. R. Moulton, 2000, Austin, TX: PRO-ED. Copyright 2000 by PRO-ED, Inc. Adapted with permission.

Name _____   Date _____

Accommodations List

☀ **Put a ✓ beside the accommodations you need.**

☐   **1.** Transportation and special parking privileges

☐   **2.** Telecommunications

☐   **3.** Mobility training (e.g., for getting to and from job)

☐   **4.** Aided/augmentative communication devices

☐   **5.** Daily-living attendant

☐   **6.** Computer with appropriate software (e.g., word processing with spelling and grammar checks)

☐   **7.** Note taker or copy of notes for school

☐   **8.** American Sign Language interpreter

☐   **9.** Books on tape

☐ **10.** Simplified directions

☐ **11.** Enlarged print

☐ **12.** Curriculum adaptations

☐ **13.** More time on tests

☐ **14.** Adjustments in the amount of work required for school assignments

☐ **15.** Building, house, or apartment accessibility

☐ **16.** Restroom accessibility

☐ **17.** Assistive sport resources

☐ **18.** Special diet

☐ **19.** Special lighting

☐ **20.** Adaptive or special furniture

☐ **21.** Special acoustics

☐ **22.** Special seating arrangement with minimal distractions

☐ **23.** Special rest periods

Source: Self-Advocacy Strategy for Education and Transition Planning (p. 171), by A. K. Van Reusen, C. Bos, J. B. Schumaker, and D. D. Deshler, 1994, Lawrence, KS: Edge Enterprises. Copyright 1994 by A. K. Van Reusen, C. Bos, J. B. Schumaker, and D. D. Deshler. Adapted with permission.

Name _____ Date _____

Accommodations for Learning Difficulties

☀ **Select the accommodations that will improve your learning.**

Accommodations for Reading Difficulties

❏ Ask to have textbooks taped

❏ Ask for a reader service (usually coordinated by Students with Disabilities Service offices)

❏ Ask to have tests and exams read aloud to you

❏ Ask for study guides, such as outlines, so you can focus your attention on essential information in textbooks

❏ Ask for extra time to complete reading assignments

❏ Underline or highlight the key points in your textbooks

❏ Work in a quiet study area

❏ Let the teacher know before the class starts that you feel uncomfortable reading aloud

❏ Choose classes carefully so there is a mix of reading required (some heavy reading, some lighter reading)

❏ Participate in reading skills classes

❏ Request a peer tutor to go through and review important points of class discussion and textbooks with you to help highlight essential information

Accommodations for Writing Difficulties

❏ Learn and use word processing with spelling, grammar, and editor checks

❏ Ask for proofreading help

❏ Dictate written work

❏ Ask for alternative assignments such as oral presentations or demonstrations

❏ Ask for a note taker in lecture classes

❏ Tape record lectures

Accommodations for Math Difficulties

❏ Sit in the front of class

❏ Ask for explanation of symbols or steps if not sure

❏ In your notes, list steps to a process

❏ Set up time to consult with teacher outside of class, if you have questions

❏ Work with a peer tutor

❏ Use graph paper to line up problems correctly

❏ Ask the teacher for concrete examples

❏ Ask for extra time

❏ Use a calculator

Accommodations for Organizational Difficulties

❏ Ask for a syllabus before the class begins

❏ Ask for a schedule of assignments for the semester at the beginning of class or before class begins

❏ Ask for copy of PowerPoint slides before class begins

❏ Ask for directions to be repeated when needed; don't leave class until you understand

❏ Set up time to see the teacher individually for clarification

Source: Tools for Transition: Student Handbook (p. 10), by American Guidance Service, Inc., 1991, Circle Pines, MN: Author. Copyright 1991 by AGS. Adapted with permission.

Accommodations for My Learning Style

Name _____   Date _____

☼ Identify areas related to learning that are problems for you, and then identify accommodations that might help.

Personal Areas Needing Support	Possible Accommodations

Source: Tools for Transition: Student Handbook (p. 14), by American Guidance Service, Inc., 1991, Circle Pines, MN: Author. Copyright 1991 by AGS. Adapted with permission.

Name _____

Date _____

Assistive Technology Self-Evaluation

☼ **Select a task and respond in each column with information about useful technology. Use the information on the following two pages to help you complete this form.**

☐ **Math**   ☐ **Reading**   ☐ **Writing**   ☐ **Listening**   ☐ **Communication**   ☐ **Studying/Organizing**

☐ **Physical Access to Instruction**   ☐ **Manipulating Materials**   ☐ **Other**

A	B	C	D	E
What difficulties do you experience in school?	What strategies, materials, equipment, and technology tools have you already used?	What new or additional assistive technology or accommodations should you consider and try?	How will you know if the technology works?	Did the assistive technology work, and how did you feel about using it?

Source: *Assistive Technology Self-Evaluation Guide for Students with Learning Disabilities* (n.d.), by LDOnline.org. Retrieved January 25, 2008, from www.ldonline.org/article/8088 Adapted with permission.

Column A

- ◼ What difficulties do you experience in school?

- ◼ What are your strengths and limitations?

- ◼ What educational tasks are you unable to perform because of your disability?

- ◼ Will the use of assistive technology enable you to overcome your limitations?

Column B

- ◼ What strategies, materials, equipment, and technology tools have you already used to address concerns? (See Examples of Assistive Technology on the next page for more information.)

Column C

- ◼ What new or additional assistive technology or accommodations should you try?

- ◼ What is your prior experience with technology, and do you want to use assistive technology?

- ◼ How are you to be involved in the decision-making process to determine the most appropriate assistive technology?

- ◼ What are your expectations for what assistive technology will do for you?

- ◼ Are your teachers comfortable with the assistive technology you are trying? If not, will training and support be available for them?

Column D

- ◼ How will you know whether or not your needs are being met with this new assistive technology?

- ◼ What is the plan to use the technology in class?

- ◼ Who will help you implement a plan?

- ◼ When will you decide whether or not the assistive technology is working?

- ◼ Does the use of assistive technology meet your IEP goals?

- ◼ Are you using the assistive technology? If not, why not?

Column E

- ◼ Did the assistive technology help in completing the task, and how did you feel about using it?

- ◼ Is there an increase in school work completed? How much?

- ◼ Is there a change in time spent completing school work? How much?

- ◼ Are there consequences of using the assistive technology? What are they?

- ◼ How do you feel about using the assistive technology, and why?

Source: Assistive Technology Self-Evaluation Guide for Students with Learning Disabilities (n.d.), by LDOnline.org. Retrieved January 25, 2008 from www.ldonline.org/article/8088 Adapted with permission.

Task	No Tech	Low Tech	High Tech
Math	• Graph paper • Post-it notes to track place value	• Calculator • Modified paper (enlarged, raised line)	• Software w/template for computation • Hand-held talking calculator
Reading	• 3 × 5 cards to mark reading	• Changes in text size • Changes in background color	• Electronic books • Screen readers • Optical Character Recognition
Writing (Spelling)	• Dictionary • Graphic organizers	• Slant board • Alternate keyboard • Electronic Spellcheck • Tape recorder	• Word processor • Word prediction software • Laptop computer • Semantic organizers
Listening	• Preferential seating in class	• Tape recorder • Note taker	• FM amplification device • Laptop computer for note-taking • Compact word processor for note-taking • Variable speech control tape recorder
Communication	• Communication board • Alphabetical board • Pen and paper	• Tape recorder to practice what you are saying	• Sign language interpreter • Computerized communication system • Alpha Smart
Studying/Organizing	• Aids for organizing material • Highlighter • Index cards • Ear plugs	• Appointment book • Beeper/Buzzers • Graphic organizer worksheets	• Software for organization of ideas • Variable speech control • Tape recorders • Electronic organizer (i.e., Palm Pilot)
Physical Access to Instruction	• Classroom arrangement • High tables • Low shelves	• Ramps • Railings	• Electric wheelchair • Helping dogs
Manipulating Materials	• Grabber • Ask a friend • Rubber fingers	• Book holder	• Scanner to present written word without e-mail attachments turning pages • Page turner
Other _____ _____	_____ _____ _____	_____ _____ _____	_____ _____ _____

Source: *Assistive Technology Self-Evaluation Guide for Students with Learning Disabilities* (n.d.), by LDOnline.org. Retrieved January 25, 2008 from www.ldonline.org/article/8088
Adapted with permission.

Name _____   Date _____

Accommodations by Functional Need

☼ **Check the accommodations that would be helpful to you.**

Reading

____ Extra time

____ Shorter assignments

____ Another person to read material aloud

____ Large print

____ Larger type face used while word processing

____ Read along with audiotaped material

____ Talking calculator

____ Change of lighting source and/or intensity of light

____ Speech synthesis software for reading on a computer screen

Accessing Information with Low Vision

____ Low-vision treatment

____ Magnification devices

____ Large, bolded-print text and materials

____ Extra time

____ Sitting closer to materials that must be viewed (blackboard, posters, overheads, etc.)

____ Yellow acetate overlays to enhance print contrast

____ An assistant to read and/or audiotape items

____ Audiotaped presentations

____ Computer with a larger screen

____ Color-coded keys on calculator or keyboard

____ Adapted computer software, such as ZoomText

____ Change of lighting source and/or intensity of light

____ Use of adjustable lamp/light source

____ Brimmed cap worn to reduce glare

____ Computer with voice recognition capabilities

Accessing Information with No Vision

____ Braille texts

____ Slate and stylus or brailler for Braille writing

____ Allowed to read/study at home, where equipment/ technology is available that is not available in the classroom

____ An assistant to read and/or audio tape items

____ Computer with voice recognition capabilities

____ Print scanner

Handwriting

____ Use of an alphabet chart

____ Alternate methods of holding the writing utensil

____ Adaptive devices such as grips, rulers, guides, paper with raised lines, or universal cuff

____ Paper stabilizing device (transparent tape, paper weight, etc.)

____ Typing or using word processing rather than writing

____ Computer with speech recognition capabilities

____ Use of key guard to prevent multiple simultaneous keystrokes

____ Different writing utensils (felt-tip pen, pen, pencil, oversized pencil)

____ Different writing surfaces such as different types of paper, more than one layer, or sandpaper underneath the paper

____ Graph paper or wide-lined paper

____ More time or no time limits

____ Shortened work intervals, with breaks

____ Scribe or tape recorder

➡

Source: Accommodations: Accommodating Adults with Disabilities in Adult Education Programs, by University of Kansas Institute for Adult Studies, 1998, Lawrence: Author. Copyright 1998 by University of Kansas Center for Research on Learning. Adapted with permission.

Solving Math Problems

____ Shorter assignments

____ Manipulatives (blocks, paper clips, etc.)

____ Extra time to complete assignments and/or tests

____ Shortened work intervals

____ Use of an abacus

____ Computer software and/or calculator

____ Graph paper

____ Vertically lined paper

Attention to Oral Directions

____ Smaller, more distinct steps

____ Provided with written copy of oral directions and lectures

____ Repeat directions orally, or use a written cue

____ Visual cues on chalkboard or overhead

____ Checklist of steps

____ Pictorial diagrams

Attention to Task

____ Use carrel or quiet corner to free the work area from distractions

____ Use of sound-absorbing devices

____ More time to complete assignments and/or tests

____ Audiotapes

____ Shortened time periods of desk work

____ Use of timer

____ Breaks and/or physical movement during breaks

____ Work with a partner who cues you to stay on task

____ Use of white noise

Staying on Track

____ Specified time frame for assignment/task completion

____ Color coding

____ Visual cues

____ Keep materials/assignments in file folders

____ Work on only one subject at a time

____ Checklists to keep track of assignments

____ Use of a backpack or briefcase to keep things together

____ Use of a computer to keep track of assignments

Dealing with Change

____ Outline of day's plan

____ Daily routine posted with changes discussed as soon as possible

____ Time to acclimate to new areas, classroom space, new staff, and new students

____ Clear, predictable breaks between activities

Remembering

____ Make cue notes

____ Write all assignments in an assignment book

____ Step by step checklists for completing assignments

____ Tasks are demonstrated

____ Assignments are listed with their instructions on the blackboard

Frustration

____ Shortened work intervals

____ More time to complete assignments and/or tests

____ Frequent breaks that allow physical movement

____ Use of soft, relaxing music (if it is not distracting to others)

____ Use of carrel or quiet corner to free the work area from distractions

____ Allowed to se up own schedule

Accessing Information with Impaired Hearing

____ Written copy of oral directions and lectures provided

____ Use of a microphone/amplifier combination

____ Visual cues such as flashing lights for timed tasks

____ Placed in close proximity to the person speaking

____ Person speaking is right in front of you

____ Interpreters

____ Compressed speech

____ Elimination of background noise

➲

Source: Accommodations: Accommodating Adults with Disabilities in Adult Education Programs, by University of Kansas Institute for Adult Studies, 1998, Lawrence: Author. Copyright 1998 by University of Kansas Center for Research on Learning. Adapted with permission.

Accessing Information with No Hearing

____ Written copy of oral directions and lectures provided

____ Signing, lip reading, and/or an interpreter

____ Visual cues on chalkboard or overhead

____ Group discussions held in semicircle so the person with a hearing impairment can see everyone that is speaking

____ Person speaking is right in front of you, if lip reading

Expressing Self Verbally

____ Alternative forms of information sharing (e.g., taped instead of oral reports, demonstrations, debates)

____ Extra time to respond to questions

____ Computer synthesized speech software

____ Communications board

____ Signing or using an interpreter

____ Responses given in demonstration of written format

____ Organizational aids (i.e., cue cards, overhead, etc.)

____ Use of a study partner

Accessing Facilities with Low or No Vision

____ Braille maps of facilities

____ Layout of classroom is taught on first day of class

____ Brightly colored tape to enhance the visibility of small objects

____ Room arrangement is kept constant

____ Colored tape to enhance contrast of desk edges and other protruding objects in the classroom

____ Cords and other hindrances stored away from traveled areas

Assessing Facilities in a Wheelchair

____ Adjusted heights of tables and desks

____ Widened doors and aisles

____ Cords and other hindrances stored away from traveled areas

Sitting Tolerance: Sitting Increases Agitation and Distraction from Task

____ Use of fidget objects to relieve tension (paper clips, small balls, etc.)

____ Food allowed in classroom

____ Chewing gum, licorice, lollipops, etc.

____ Wearing comfortable clothes

____ Different kinds of chairs used (e.g., beanbag, rocking chair, therapy ball)

____ Sitting close to the instructor

____ Lighting changes

____ Temperature changes

____ Frequent breaks that allow physical movement

Sitting Tolerance: Sitting Causes Pain or Fatigue

____ Stand up or lie down when necessary

____ Extra time to complete assignments and/or tests

____ Use of a lumbar support chair and /or footstool

____ Work on assignments at home, where more comfortable, and check in by phone or e-mail

____ Changing positions every 10–15 minutes to prevent pain and fatigue

Source: Accommodations: Accommodating Adults with Disabilities in Adult Education Programs, by University of Kansas Institute for Adult Studies, 1998, Lawrence: Author. Copyright 1998 by University of Kansas Center for Research on Learning. Adapted with permission.

Name _____   Date _____

Test Preparation and Test Taking

☀ **Check the appropriate space to indicate whether or not you typically prepare for and take tests as described.**

Prior to the Exam

	Yes	No
I review all notes, reading and homework assignments, etc.	____	____
I make up a practice test from class notes and other materials and quiz myself.	____	____
I answer the practice quiz questions without looking at my notes.	____	____
I refine my answers to quiz questions.	____	____
I use a systematic study method (e.g., SQ4R) to review reading assignments.	____	____
I take short breaks between study sessions.	____	____
I follow a weekly study schedule.	____	____
I get plenty of sleep the night before an exam.	____	____

During the Exam

	Yes	No
I read the instructions for the exam carefully before I begin.	____	____
I determine how I will schedule my time for each part of the exam.	____	____
I read each question on the exam carefully.	____	____
I ask the instructor to clarify questions that I do not understand.	____	____
I determine how I will schedule my time for each part of the exam..........................	____	____
I leave myself some time at the end of the exam to review my answers.	____	____
I outline answers to essay questions before I begin to write.	____	____
I make sure my answers to essay questions have an introductory and concluding paragraph.	____	____
I try to write legibly.	____	____
I am careful about spelling, grammar, and punctuation.	____	____
If I begin to get nervous on an exam, I use relaxation techniques to calm myself down.	____	____

Source: Self-Management for College Students: The ABC Approach (2nd ed., pp. 166–167), by E. J. O'Keefe and D. S . Berger, 1999, Hyde Park, NY: Partridge Hill Publishers. Copyright 1999 by Partridge Hill Publishers. Adapted with permission.

Name _____ Date _____

Methods for Maintaining Academic Motivation

☀ **Complete each of the following three areas.**

❶ Rank the following methods for maintaining the **cognitive aspects** of positive motivation in order of personal preference. Place 1 next to your first preference, 2 next to your second preference, etc.

_____ a. Visualizing rewards

_____ b. Supportive self-talk

_____ c. Imagining success

_____ d. Recalling past achievements

_____ e. Attaining goals

❷ Rank the following methods for maintaining the **affective aspects** of academic motivation in order of personal preference. Place 1 next to your first preference, 2 next to your second preference, etc.

_____ a. Getting adequate rest

_____ b. Exercising regularly

_____ c. Maintaining a balanced diet

_____ d. Practicing relaxation

_____ e. Engaging in nonacademic recreation

❸ Rank the following methods for maintaining the **behavioral aspects** of academic motivation in order of personal preference. Place 1 next to your first preference, 2 next to your second preference, etc. Cross out any behavior that you refuse to do to maintain your academic motivation. Do not include these behaviors in your ranking.

_____ a. Dressing appropriately for class

_____ b. Sitting in the front of the class

_____ c. Asking questions and participating in class discussions

_____ d. Talking to friends about course readings, topics, etc.

_____ e. Reading a newspaper each day

_____ f. Reading a news magazine each week

_____ g. Watching a news program on television every day

_____ h. Watching educational programming each week

_____ i. Attending cultural events on and off campus

_____ j. Talking to professors outside of class

_____ k. Participating in a campus club or society

_____ l. Visiting historical sites, museums, art galleries, etc.

Source: Source: Self-Management for College Students: The ABC Approach (2nd ed., p. 285), by E. J. O'Keefe and D. S. Berger, 1999, Hyde Park, NY: Partridge Hill Publishers. Copyright 1999 by Partridge Hill Publishers. Adapted with permission.

Nonacademic Support Needs: Examining the Other Parts of My Life

List of Inventories

Name _____   Date _____

Cost-of-Living Analysis: Semester

☀ **Develop a semester budget for ongoing college expenses. Consider two options: "Lean" budget and "Luxury" budget.**

		Lean	Luxury
❶	Tuition	_____	_____
❷	Room and board	_____	_____
❸	Books and supplies	_____	_____
❹	Transportation (home to school)	_____	_____
❺	Medical and health	_____	_____
❻	Insurance	_____	_____
❼	Personal expenses		
	Clothing	_____	_____
	Food/Meals	_____	_____
	Room furnishings	_____	_____
	Social/Recreational/Entertainment	_____	_____
	Personal care (hair, toothpaste)	_____	_____
	Laundry	_____	_____
	Telephone (basic services)	_____	_____
	Telephone (text messaging, etc.)	_____	_____
	Snacks	_____	_____
	Transportation around campus	_____	_____
	Sports or lab fees	_____	_____
	Cable	_____	_____
	Other		
	_____	_____	_____
	_____	_____	_____
	_____	_____	_____

Source: College Comes Sooner Than You Think! (pp. 122–123), by B. D. Featherstone and J. M. Reilly, 1990, Dayton, OH: Ohio Psychology Press. Copyright 1990 by Ohio Psychology Press. Adapted with permission.

Name _____ Date _____

Individual Accommodations

☼ Use this form to help you deal with everyday events that might be problematic in your life as a student.

	Is this a problem for me?			
Activity	**Yes**	**Somewhat**	**No**	**Possible Solutions**

Getting to Campus

Using public transportation

1. Locating parking and transit office ☐ ☐ ☐ _____

2. Entering building ☐ ☐ ☐ _____

3. Maneuvering to parking and transit counter ☐ ☐ ☐ _____

4. Communicating with parking and transit employees ☐ ☐ ☐ _____

5. Receiving bus pass ☐ ☐ ☐ _____

6. Obtaining bus route flyers ☐ ☐ ☐ _____

7. Locating bus route nearest home ☐ ☐ ☐ _____

8. Using bus route ☐ ☐ ☐ _____

Using private transportation

1. Locating university off-campus parking lot ☐ ☐ ☐ _____

2. Acquiring university off-campus bus schedules ☐ ☐ ☐ _____

3. Arriving at university off-campus parking lot before bus comes ☐ ☐ ☐ _____

4. Parking ☐ ☐ ☐ _____

5. Maneuvering to bus waiting area ☐ ☐ ☐ _____

6. Transferring onto bus ☐ ☐ ☐ _____

7. Locating ramp or lot on campus ☐ ☐ ☐ _____

8. Preparing appropriate amount of money to pay in timed lot ☐ ☐ ☐ _____

9. Paying meter or attendant at appropriate time, if needed ☐ ☐ ☐ _____

Source: I.A.A.M.: Student Activity Checklist (pp. 3–8), by R. O. Smith, J. Warnke, D. Edyburn, D. Mellard, N. Kurth, and G. Berry, 2002, Lawrence: University of Kansas Center for Research on Learning, Division of Adult Studies. Copyright 2002 by University of Kansas Center for Research on Learning. Adapted with permission.

Activity	**Is this a problem for me?**			Possible Solutions
	Yes	Somewhat	No	

Meeting with a Counselor or Advisor

Calling counselor or advisor

1. Obtaining phone number to set up meeting	☐	☐	☐	_____
2. Dialing phone number	☐	☐	☐	_____
3. Communicating to set up date and time for meeting	☐	☐	☐	_____

Going to his or her office

1. Finding the building	☐	☐	☐	_____
2. Entering the building	☐	☐	☐	_____
3. Finding the room	☐	☐	☐	_____
4. Entering the room	☐	☐	☐	_____
5. Communicating with counselor or advisor	☐	☐	☐	_____

Meeting

1. Communication issues	☐	☐	☐	_____
2. Obtaining information	☐	☐	☐	_____
3. Deciding on classes to take	☐	☐	☐	_____
4. Helping plan your class schedule	☐	☐	☐	_____

Obtaining and Completing the Admission Form

1. Requesting information from the university (e-mail or phone)	☐	☐	☐	_____
2. Obtaining phone numbers and addresses	☐	☐	☐	_____
3. Engaging in appropriate conversational or writing style	☐	☐	☐	_____
4. Completing the admission form	☐	☐	☐	_____
5. Completing the form accurately and legibly	☐	☐	☐	_____
6. Delivering forms to admissions office through the mail or in person	☐	☐	☐	_____

Registration

Forms

1. Obtaining the registration forms	☐	☐	☐	_____
2. Registering	☐	☐	☐	_____
3. Completing the forms accurately and legibly	☐	☐	☐	_____
4. Signing up for classes recommended	☐	☐	☐	_____
5. Delivering the form to the registrar through the mail, in person, or via computer	☐	☐	☐	_____

Source: I.A.A.M.: Student Activity Checklist (pp. 3–8), by R. O. Smith, J. Warnke, D. Edyburn, D. Mellard, N. Kurth, and G. Berry, 2002, Lawrence: University of Kansas Center for Research on Learning, Division of Adult Studies. Copyright 2002 by University of Kansas Center for Research on Learning. Adapted with permission.

Activity	Is this a problem for me?			Possible Solutions
	Yes	Somewhat	No	

Obtaining an identification or activity card

1. Contacting the registration office ☐ ☐ ☐ _____

2. Finding the building ☐ ☐ ☐ _____

3. Entering the building ☐ ☐ ☐ _____

4. Finding the office ☐ ☐ ☐ _____

5. Finding and communicating with registration office staff ☐ ☐ ☐ _____

6. Getting photo taken ☐ ☐ ☐ _____

7. Completing the necessary forms ☐ ☐ ☐ _____

8. Obtaining a class schedule ☐ ☐ ☐ _____

Paying Tuition

1. Obtaining financial aid information ☐ ☐ ☐ _____

2. Obtaining scholarship information ☐ ☐ ☐ _____

3. Obtaining payment information and schedule ☐ ☐ ☐ _____

Buying Books and Supplies

Going to the bookstore

1. Finding the bookstore ☐ ☐ ☐ _____

2. Entering the bookstore ☐ ☐ ☐ _____

3. Maneuvering around the bookstore ☐ ☐ ☐ _____

Buying books

1. Arriving at the ground level in the bookstore ☐ ☐ ☐ _____

2. Having class schedules available ☐ ☐ ☐ _____

3. Finding the aisles ☐ ☐ ☐ _____

4. Getting the books off the shelves ☐ ☐ ☐ _____

5. Transporting the books ☐ ☐ ☐ _____

6. Arriving at the appropriate floor to pay ☐ ☐ ☐ _____

7. Finding the register ☐ ☐ ☐ _____

8. Maneuvering to the register ☐ ☐ ☐ _____

9. Placing the books and or supplies on the counter ☐ ☐ ☐ _____

10. Paying for the items ☐ ☐ ☐ _____

11. Transporting the books out of the bookstore ☐ ☐ ☐ _____

12. Leaving the bookstore ☐ ☐ ☐ _____

Source: I.A.A.M.: Student Activity Checklist (pp. 3–8), by R. O. Smith, J. Warnke, D. Edyburn, D. Mellard, N. Kurth, and G. Berry, 2002, Lawrence: University of Kansas Center for Research on Learning, Division of Adult Studies. Copyright 2002 by University of Kansas Center for Research on Learning. Adapted with permission.

Activity	Is this a problem for me?			Possible Solutions
	Yes	Somewhat	No	

Classes

Going to class

		Yes	Somewhat	No	
1.	Leaving at an appropriate time to get to class	☐	☐	☐	_____
2.	Finding the building on the campus map	☐	☐	☐	_____
3.	Entering the building	☐	☐	☐	_____
4.	Finding the classroom	☐	☐	☐	_____
5.	Finding a seat that accommodates your needs	☐	☐	☐	_____

Source: I.A.A.M.: Student Activity Checklist (pp. 3–8), by R. O. Smith, J. Warnke, D. Edyburn, D. Mellard, N. Kurth, and G. Berry, 2002, Lawrence: University of Kansas Center for Research on Learning, Division of Adult Studies. Copyright 2002 by University of Kansas Center for Research on Learning. Adapted with permission.

Name _____   Date _____

A Look at Where I Am Now

☀ **Place a ✓ by the statements that describe you or your skills right now.**

Personal Characteristics

_____ I have a positive attitude about school.

_____ I can adapt to changes in rules, schedules, or routine.

_____ I know the rules of the school for behavior.

_____ I know the policies of the school about graduation and testing.

_____ I use good communication skills with teachers.

_____ I have good time management skills

_____ I organize myself for what I need to do.

_____ I have a clear sense of my goal for the future.

_____ I can manage my life without my parents.

_____ I know when and how to ask for help.

_____ I have a strong commitment to finishing school.

Academic/School Success Skills

_____ I have self-advocacy skills.

_____ I have note-taking skills.

_____ I have good study skills.

_____ I have good test-taking skills.

_____ I know the importance of completing assignments and turning them in on time.

_____ I know the importance of organizing my school work (class notes and handouts).

_____ I show respect for the instructor, teaching assistant, and others in my classes.

Social Skills

_____ I interact appropriately with teachers and other students.

_____ I know how to introduce myself to a teacher or student I do not know.

_____ I know how to let someone know that I like him/her and would like to spend time together.

_____ I know how to interact with others in social situations.

_____ I know how to deal appropriately with social rejection.

_____ I know how to use public and cell phones appropriately.

Independent Living Skills

_____ I know how to use transportation alternatives.

_____ I use my leisure time effectively.

_____ I know how to locate the help and assistance I need in the community.

_____ I can manage my health needs.

_____ I can manage my money.

_____ I can manage my laundry, shopping, and home responsibilities.

Source: Effective College Planning (5th ed., p. 10), by WNY Collegiate Consortium of Disability Advocates, 1997, Erie, PA: Author. Copyright 1997 by WNY Collegiate Consortium of Disability Advocates. Adapted with permission.

Name _____   Date _____

Basic Survival Skills

☀ **Place a ✓ in the boxes beside the statements that describe you.**

Health Care

❑ Know when to seek medical care
❑ Know where to seek medical care on campus
❑ Aware of any allergies to medications
❑ Know about student health insurance coverage
❑ Know basic first aid skills

Daily Living

❑ Understand the potential risks of using a credit card
❑ Know how to budget money
❑ Know how to distinguish between wants and needs
❑ Know how to do laundry
❑ Know how to fix simple foods
❑ Practice good hygiene skills
❑ Know how to locate buildings on campus for classes

Social Skills and Recreation

❑ Respect others' privacy
❑ Respect others' property
❑ Respond appropriately to peer pressure
❑ Have a hobby or special interest that others might also enjoy
❑ Know how to access the Student Union
❑ Know how to access recreational events on campus
❑ Have identified someone with whom to confide

Time Management

❑ Know how to use an alarm clock
❑ Get up in time for classes
❑ Get to classes on time
❑ Complete assignments on time
❑ Plan ahead for projects that are due
❑ Use a planner (print or computer based)

Source: Copyright 2008 by G. M. Clark. Adapted with permission.

Name _____   Date _____

Home-Living Assessment

☼ **Check out your level of competence in the following daily living areas.**

Rating Scale: I do (or _____ does) this
0 = *No, or no experience in this area*
1 = *Yes, with help or modifications*
2 = *Yes, no problem*

	Student	Parent

Self-Care

1. Do you have good sleeping habits and get enough sleep. . . . . ____ ____

2. Do you take good care of yourself when you get sick? . . . . ____ ____

3. When you are having personal problems, do you go to friends or
family members for help? . . . . ____ ____

4. Do you have good health habits, like avoiding tobacco, too much
alcohol, or harmful drugs? . . . . ____ ____

5. Do you have good personal grooming and hygiene habits?. . . . . ____ ____

Nutrition and Fitness

6. Do you eat well-balanced, healthy meals each day? . . . . ____ ____

7. Do you limit the amount of junk food you eat? . . . . ____ ____

8. Do you maintain your weight at a good level?. . . . . ____ ____

9. Do you exercise at least three times a week? . . . . ____ ____

Personal Management

10. Do you get yourself up in the morning?. . . . . ____ ____

11. Do you prepare meals for yourself? . . . . ____ ____

12. Do you manage money effectively?. . . . . ____ ____

13. Do you manage time effectively? . . . . ____ ____

14. Do you perform routine household maintenance chores
(washing dishes, cleaning, replacing light bulbs, etc.)?. . . . . ____ ____

15. Do you choose and care for your clothes?. . . . . ____ ____

16. Do you use basic tools, like a hammer, pliers, or screwdriver
to fix things around the house?. . . . . ____ ____

➥

Source: Transition Skills Assessment (pp. 3–4), by Minnesota Interagency Office on Transition Services, 1996, St. Paul, MN: Author. Copyright 1996 by Minnesota Offices on Transition Services. Adapted with permission.

	Student	Parent

Money Management

17. Do you pay for things in stores without making mistakes? (e.g., know if you have enough money to buy what you want, know if you get the correct change) .... _____ _____

18. Do you shop carefully and get things for good prices? .... _____ _____

19. Do you use a checking or savings account to manage your money? .... _____ _____

20. Do you budget your money well enough to pay for the things you want and need? .... _____ _____

Medical

21. Do you know what to do in emergency situations? .... _____ _____

22. Do you independently take medication? .... _____ _____

23. Do you make doctor's appointments? .... _____ _____

24. Do you know the difference between serious and minor illnesses? .... _____ _____

25. If you have a disability, can you explain it to medical personnel? .... _____ _____

Note. You should consider taking some action for any statement for which you responded with a "0."

Source: Transition Skills Assessment (pp. 3–4), by Minnesota Interagency Office on Transition Services, 1996, St. Paul, MN: Author. Copyright 1996 by Minnesota Offices on Transition Services. Adapted with permission.

Independent-Living Skills

☀ **Circle Yes or No in response to each of the following statements.**

Can you...

1. Organize and maintain possessions?	Yes	No
2. Bathe and groom self regularly?	Yes	No
3. Select clothes appropriately (choosing colors, styles, bargains)?	Yes	No
4. Interpret weather information, and dress accordingly?	Yes	No
5. Wash, dry, and iron clothes?	Yes	No
6. Plan and cook balanced meals?	Yes	No
7. Store food, package and use leftovers?	Yes	No
8. Read and follow label directions?	Yes	No
9. Use cleaning materials safely?	Yes	No
10. Store hazardous materials and medicines?	Yes	No
11. Shop for food and other living items?	Yes	No
12. Operate other household appliances (e.g., oven, microwave, dishwasher, vacuum)?	Yes	No
13. Operate entertainment devices (e.g., TV, Tivo, recorders)?	Yes	No
14. Clean apartment/house?	Yes	No
15. Decorate and maintain an apartment/house?	Yes	No
16. Make basic home repairs?	Yes	No
17. Arrange for garbage/trash collection and utility services (i.e., water, gas, electricity, telephone)?	Yes	No
18. Keep and use a calendar/planner?	Yes	No
19. Use a telephone and telephone directory including the yellow pages?	Yes	No
20. Ask for and give directions?	Yes	No
21. Use public transportation and read schedules?	Yes	No
22. Drive a car?	Yes	No
23. Maintain a car and fix a flat tire?	Yes	No
24. Read a map and interpret road signs?	Yes	No
25. Plan and take a trip?	Yes	No
26. Develop and maintain an exercise schedule?	Yes	No

Appendix: Support for Accommodation Request

Support for Accommodation Request

Student's Name _____

ID # _____

1. **Eligibility/Diagnostic Statement**
   - Date of original eligibility
   - Most recent reevaluation date
   - Current goal area(s) of concern

2. **Formal Diagnosis and Date** (When available)

3. **Basis of Determination for Current Services**
   (Provide available formal/informal diagnostic assessment information and recent evaluation results, include performance levels with/without accommodations.)

4. **Current Functional Impact of the Disability** (Please describe)

5. **Response to Specially Designed Instructional Intervention**

6. **Expected Progression or Stability of the Disability**

7. **History of Accommodations**
   - 8th Grade
   - 9th Grade
   - 10th Grade
   - 11th Grade
   - 12th Grade

8. **Suggested Accommodations for Postsecondary Experiences**

9. **Signature** _____

   Name of Person Completing Form (Print) _____

   Title/Role_____ Telephone_____

   Signature _____ Date _____

10. **Authorization for Release of Information**
    I hereby authorize the release of information summarized in this Support for Accommodation Request for the purpose of evaluating eligibility and accommodation requests.

    Name of Student (Print) _____

    Student's Signature _____ Date_____

11. **Student Written Response—Statement of Goals** (Please write your statement of at least 3–5 sentences describing what you hope to accomplish in the next year.)

Source: Support for Accommodation Request, by Iowa Department of Education, 2005, Des Moines: Author. Copyright 2005 by Iowa Department of Education. Adapted with permission.

Support for Accommodation Request

Student's Name ___Heather___

ID # ___N/A___

1. **Eligibility/Diagnostic Statement**
   - Date of original eligibility   March 24, 1999
   - Most recent reevaluation date   March 2, 2005
   - Current goal area(s) of concern

   Heather continues to be eligible to receive special education services as an Eligible Individual (noncategorical) for instruction in Math, Reading, and Written Language.

2. **Formal Diagnosis and Date** (When available)

   Heather was diagnosed as an Entitled/Eligible Individual on March 24, 1999.

3. **Basis of Determination for Current Services**

   (Provide available formal/informal diagnostic assessment information and recent evaluation results, include performance levels with/without accommodations.)

   Discrepancy from peers based on ITED (November 2004):
   - Math concepts & problem solving
     Composite–64th national percentile; Problem Solving–50th national percentile; Computation–4th national percentile
   - Revising written materials
     Composite–26th national percentile; Spelling–20th national percentile
   - Reading Comprehension
     Composite–15th national percentile; Vocabulary–19th national percentile

   Discrepancy from peers based on Scholastic Reading Inventory (SRI) taken 10/21/05:
   - Reading Lexile Score = 11th percentile; 3rd Stanine

4. **Current Functional Impact of the Disability** (Please describe)

   Heather has difficulty acquiring new concepts in math. She withdrew from Algebra II after one quarter because she struggles with recalling prior knowledge about how to apply new mathematical concepts and difficulty recalling basic algebraic concepts needed to solve difficult problems. She requires additional direct instruction in the form of reteaching, practice, and feedback to fully understand new material and how to use a calculator for problem solving.

   Heather requires additional reading and writing support in content-area classes to move through the general education curriculum. She was successful in the general education curriculum in reading, writing, and math when she had extra time to complete assignments and tests and when tests were read out loud. Resource support has benefited Heather by having her proofread her work, ask questions, and receive additional instruction on concepts she did not fully comprehend during the whole-class instruction. Heather is most successful when she feels comfortable discussing her disabilities with the teacher and asking for help during and outside of class. However, Heather struggles with being a self-advocate and will often leave class without understanding important concepts or assignment direction and fails to ask for clarification in class.

Source: Support for Accommodation Request, by Iowa Department of Education, 2005, Des Moines: Author. Copyright 2005 by Iowa Department of Education. Adapted with permission.

5. Response to Specially Designed Instructional Intervention

Heather benefits from an average of 45 minutes daily direct one-on-one instructional support in a small-group setting. She is very organized but must learn self-advocacy during her senior year of high school, after relying on special education support in the general education setting in years past.

• Reading: Heather has maintained steady discrepancy from her peers in reading comprehension, averaging 11–15 percentile rank on ITED and SRI standardized tests. This discrepancy from peers is manifested in the amount of time it takes her to read content area material and complete assigned work. However, she has improved her independence in content area general education classes during her senior year by limiting her dependency for instructional support in the classroom. Instructional support in the past has included one-on-one instruction support in the general education setting from special education staff in the form of reteaching, clarification, or note-taking assistance. She elected to take college preparation classes her senior year with the accommodations of extra time, having tests read out loud, and generalized instruction support outside the general education setting. While these accommodations have shown limited success, she still struggles with taking advantage of accommodations and/or self-advocating for them if she is the only student in the room eligible for accommodations in the general education setting.

• Language: Heather has continued to maintain her discrepancy from her peers in the area of written language, maintaining a 26th percentile in Revising Written Materials on the ITED assessment. She has benefited greatly from using computer-processing software to check her grammar and spelling in her writing. However, Heather still requires instructional support in composing and editing written materials. The accommodations of extra time have been very helpful for Heather in her writing, as it costs effort and time for her to form thoughts into sentences and paragraphs (this would include essay assessments). However, as mentioned before, she has difficulty being a self-advocate for these types of accommodations during class testing time unless she has been assured that the instructor understands her learning difficulties.

• Math: Heather has decreased her discrepancy from her peers in Mathematics Concepts and Problem Solving reaching the 64th percentile on the ITED assessment. However, she has maintained her discrepancy in Mathematical Computation, scoring in the 14th percentile on the ITED assessment. She has difficulty recalling basic math facts and procedures especially in the areas of decimals/percents and fractions and benefits from the use of a calculator for recalling basic math facts in order to be successful in problem solving. She has benefited tremendously from supported direct instruction in content area math classes, usually in the form of reteaching past procedures, tutoring current concepts, and providing additional notes and formulas. However, this has also caused her to rely heavily on support and was not successful her senior year in an Algebra II class, when the instructional support was limited to resource time outside the general educational setting. This was compounded by the length of time that passed from when she learned the basics of Algebra her freshmen year and when she had taken Algebra II her senior year. Heather may require refresher classes in the future to help build confidence in her mathematical abilities as well as rebuild her understanding algebra basic concepts.

Source: Support for Accommodation Request, by Iowa Department of Education, 2005, Des Moines: Author. Copyright 2005 by Iowa Department of Education. Adapted with permission.

6. Expected Progression or Stability of the Disability

Heather continues to have difficulty in Reading, Writing, and Math, which will most likely remain stable throughout her lifetime. Her discrepancy from her peers has remained similar as her independence continues to grow. She has become more independent, but not without struggle. Her grades suffered before she adjusted to the transition of her senior year, where she experienced more intensified curricular demands without the benefit of the instructional support she had been used to in the general education setting. The transition to a postsecondary institution may also produce the similar growing pains. She will most likely continue to benefit from instructional support in some form as well as accommodations at the postsecondary level. However, she has only recently started to become a self-advocate and may still require assistance in receiving proper accommodations in a postsecondary setting.

7. History of Accommodations

- 8th Grade

Heather received accommodations in all of her classes. She was allowed extra time to complete assignments and tests and was allowed to complete homework and tests in a quiet environment. She was able to have tests read out loud. Larger assignments may have been broken down into smaller assignments. Heather was able to use a computer for checking spelling and grammar when typing writing assignments. She was also able to use a calculator for math. She was provided with specially designed instruction in the areas of reading, writing, and math. The instruction was designed in cooperation with the general education teacher and the special education teacher. This included but was not limited to small-group reteaching, assistance with completing homework, guided notes, book on tape (when available), and daily reminders of assignment expectations. Assignment and assessment modifications were made only when it was identified that Heather may not be successful otherwise (very rare). Heather has been successful using these accommodations but relied heavily on the general education teacher and special education teacher for support ensuring the accommodations were in place.

- 9th Grade   Continued

- 10th Grade   Continued

- 11th Grade   Continued

- 12th Grade

Accommodations continued. However, a lot of time was spent on developing self-advocacy skills. Specially designed instruction was limited to request for assistance from Heather for clarification to either the general education teacher or special education teacher, as she was often the only eligible student in the college prep classes.

8. Suggested Accommodations for Postsecondary Experiences

- Direct instruction in reading comprehension for word meanings, organizing, and analyzing materials: study groups, peer tutors, reading-skills or study-skills class

Source: Support for Accommodation Request, by Iowa Department of Education, 2005, Des Moines: Author. Copyright 2005 by Iowa Department of Education. Adapted with permission.

- Support in content-area classes for difficulty with reading comprehension, speed of reading, and lectures: taped texts, use of highlighters or color coding, class or textbook outlines or notes, sharing peer notes/note taker, or tape recorders

- Support for exams due to understanding questions, writing under pressure, organizing thoughts, mechanics of writing (spelling, punctuation, grammar), distractions: taped or oral exams when needed, extra time for exams, word processing option for essays, proofreading, writing assistance, separate room for testing

- Difficulty with written work due to writing notes legibly, organization, spelling, punctuation, grammar: word processing (with writing supports), proofreading, and spell check/grammar check

- Difficulty with study organization for planning for research/longer projects: calendar to plan assignment breakdowns for term and daily/weekly written study schedule

9. **Signature** _____

Name of Person Completing Form (Print) _____

Title/Role_____ Telephone_____

Signature _____ Date _____

10. **Authorization for Release of Information**
    I hereby authorize the release of information summarized in this Support for Accommodation Request for the purpose of evaluating eligibility and accommodation requests.

    Name of Student (Print) _____

    Student's Signature _____ Date_____

11. **Student Written Response—Statement of Goals** (Please write your statement of at least 3–5 sentences describing what you hope to accomplish in the next year.)

    I would like to go to college after high school to get a certificate in day care. I'm planning on going to MCC for two years. I'm also wanting to be a kendergarden or first grade teacher, but I don't think I'm going to do that b/c I would have to take harder classes and go longer than 2 years. I just want to go and get my degree or certificate in day care.

Source: Support for Accommodation Request, by Iowa Department of Education, 2005, Des Moines: Author. Copyright 2005 by Iowa Department of Education. Adapted with permission.

About the Authors

☀ **Patricia L. Sitlington,** PhD, is professor and coordinator of the graduate emphasis in Career/Vocational Programming and Transition at the University of Northern Iowa. She has been a secondary classroom teacher and state department transition staff member. She has worked with numerous states and school districts in designing and implementing transition assessment approaches and outcomes studies of students with and without disabilities, and in conducting program evaluations. She has authored a number of articles, chapters, and books in the area of transition. Her writing and research interests include assessment, postschool outcomes of young adults with and without disabilities, transition to postsecondary education and employment, and systems change.

☀ **James R. Patton,** EdD, is currently an independent consultant and adjunct associate professor in the Department of Special Education at the University of Texas at Austin. He formerly was a special education teacher, having taught students with special needs at the elementary, secondary, and postsecondary levels of schooling. He has written books, chapters, articles, and tests in the area of special education. Dr. Patton's current areas of professional interest are the assessment of the transition strengths and needs of students, the infusion of real-life content into existing curricula, study skills instruction, behavioral intervention planning, and the accommodation of students with special needs in inclusive settings. He is also working as a mental retardation forensic specialist in regard to death penalty cases in Texas and throughout the country.

☀ **Gary M. Clark,** EdD, is a professor of special education at the University of Kansas. His professional interest in adolescents with disabilities goes back to his work as a teacher, school counselor, and vocational rehabilitation counselor in Texas. He has contributed to the state transition guidelines for Kansas and Utah and has been a consultant in a number of states for career development, transition programming, life skills curricula, transition assessment, and secondary special education teacher education. Dr. Clark has authored numerous books, chapters, and tests in the area of transition planning.